Carpentry and Joinery for Building Craft Students 1

Peter Brett
Willesden College of Technology

Hutchinson

London Melbourne Sydney Auckland Johannesburg

Hutchinson & Co. (Publishers) Ltd

An imprint of the Hutchinson Publishing Group

24 Highbury Crescent, London N5 1RX

Hutchinson Group (Australia) Pty Ltd
30–32 Cremorne Street, Richmond South, Victoria 3121
PO Box 151, Broadway, New South Wales 2007

Hutchinson Group (NZ) Ltd
32–34 View Road, PO Box 40–086, Glenfield, Auckland 10

Hutchinson Group (SA) (Pty) Ltd
PO Box 337, Bergvlei 2012, South Africa

First published 1981

Set in Linoterm Times

Printed in Great Britain by The Anchor Press Ltd
and bound by Wm Brendon & Son Ltd
both of Tiptree, Essex

British Library Cataloguing in Publication Data
Brett, Peter
    Carpentry & joinery for building craft students.
    1.
    1. Carpentry
    2. Joinery
    I. Title
    694   TH5606

ISBN 0 09 143510 2 cased ✓
0 09 143511 0 paper

Contents

Preface

Carpentry and Joinery for Building Craft Students 1 is the first of two volumes designed to cover the CGLI 585 syllabus to craft certificate level.

The presentation of the books is one which will greatly aid today's building craft student. The text has been written in a clear, concise and factual style, fully integrated with numerous illustrations and photographs. Each chapter begins with a list of learning objectives and ends with a series of self-assessment questions, to which the answers are given at the back of the book. This will enable students to evaluate their understanding of the relevant chapter and to check their progress through the course. The books also have a comprehensive index for easy reference.

In addition to being ideal course textbooks for CGLI 585 students, this two-volume work will provide useful background reading for a wide range of building construction courses with a carpentry and joinery element.

Acknowledgements

The author wishes to thank the following:

Dominion Machinery Co Ltd, Wolf Electric Tools Ltd and Wadkin Ltd for supplying information on their products.

Her Majesty's Stationery Office for permission to reproduce the Woodworking Machines Regulations 1974.

I am also grateful to my wife, Christine, and two children, James and Sarah, for their help, patience and encouragement during the preparation of this book.

chapter 1

Hand tools

After reading this chapter you should be able to:

1 Name the various categories of hand tools and list a number of tools in each category.
2 Recognize different types of hand tools.
3 Select the correct tools for the work in hand.
4 Distinguish between the cutting action of various tools.
5 State the use of given tools.
6 Recognize and state the purpose of different items of site and workshop equipment.

Classification of hand tools

Woodworking hand tools can be classified in the following categories:

Saws
Planes
Wood chisels
Boring tools
Fixing tools
Marking-out tools
Workshop equipment
Site equipment
Miscellaneous items

Saws

There are various types of saw in use, each of which is designed for a specific purpose. They can be divided into three main groups:

Those used for ripping, e.g. cutting timber parallel with the grain.
Those used for cross-cutting, e.g. cutting timber across the grain.
Those used for cutting curves and shapes.

Cutting action

All saws for cutting timber have either one of two types of teeth depending on their intended use.
Ripping teeth are chisel-end teeth and the cutting action is in fact like a series of tiny chisels, each cutting one behind the other. See Figure 1.

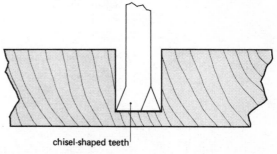

chisel-shaped teeth

Figure 1   *Ripping*

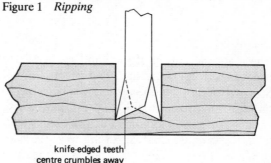

knife-edged teeth
centre crumbles away
as saw dust

Figure 2   *Cross-cutting*

Cross-cutting teeth have knife points to sever the fibres of the timber. These points are so arranged that they cut two knife lines close together. The centre fibres between these knife lines crumble away as sawdust. See Figure 2.

Note: In order to prevent the saw blade from jamming in the timber, its teeth are 'set', that is each alternate tooth is bent outwards to make a saw-cut, or kerf, which is just wide enough to clear the blade.

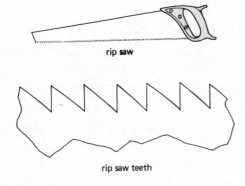

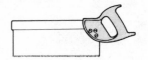

Figure 5   *Tenon saw*

Figure 3   *Rip saw*

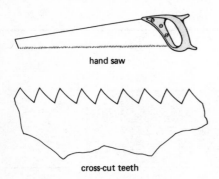

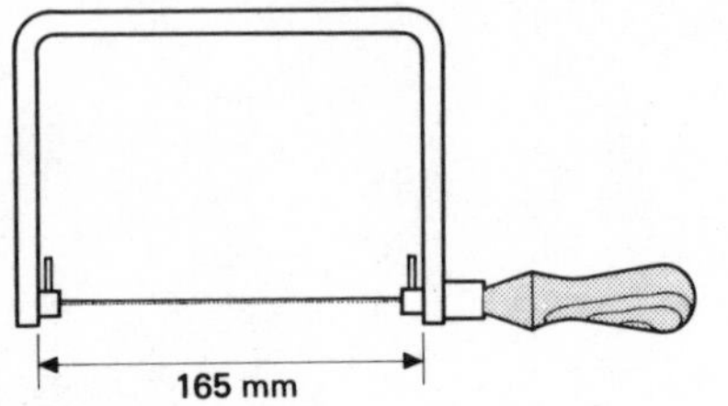

Figure 6   *Coping saw*

Figure 4   *Hand saw*

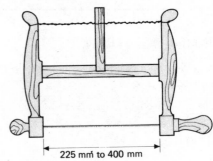

Figure 7   *Bow saw*

Rip saws (Figure 3)

These are the largest of the hand saws and are used for cutting along the grain of the timber. Much of the work of rip saws has now been mechanized, but they are still used for jobs where machines or power tools are not available or suitable. Rip saws are ideal for cutting down the sides of tenons where a tenoner is not available. The length of the rip saw blade can be up to 750 mm with 3 to 4 teeth per 25 mm.

Cross-cut saws

The *hand saw* (Figure 4) is used for rough and general purpose cross-cutting. It can be up to 650 mm long with 6 to 8 teeth per 25 mm.

The *panel saw* is used for the fine cutting of timber and sheet materials. Its length is up to 500 mm with 8 to 10 teeth per 25 mm and is similar in appearance to the hand saw.

The *tenon saw* (Figure 5) is also known as a back saw. This is because it has a folded strip of brass or steel clamped over the top edge of the blade in order to prevent it twisting or buckling during use. Its main uses are cutting shoulders for joints and fine general bench work. It is normally available up to 450 mm in length with 10 to 14 teeth per 25 mm.

The *dovetail saw* is a smaller type of tenon saw which, as its name implies, is used mainly for the cutting of dovetails. It is also used for the cutting of mouldings and other delicate work. Its length is up to 200 mm with 12 to 16 teeth per 25 mm.

Saws for cutting curves

In general, saws which are used for cutting curves have very narrow replaceable blades.

The *coping saw* (Figure 6) is a versatile all-round saw for cutting curves. Its very fine blade enables it to cut cleanly practically any shape required.

The *bow saw* (Figure 7) can cut similar curves to that of the coping saw. However, its coarser blade enables it to be used for cutting thicker material.

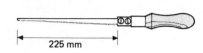

Figure 8 *Padsaw*

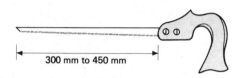

Figure 9 *Compass saw*

The *keyhole* or *padsaw* (Figure 8), as its name implies, is mainly used for cutting keyholes and other shapes and holes, away from the edge of the timber.

The *compass saw* (Figure 9) is mainly used for cutting shapes or holes which are well away from the edge of the material.

Saw maintenance

To keep a saw in good condition it should be regularly maintained. This can include one, several or all of the following operations in the order given, depending on the condition of the saw:

Topping
Shaping
Setting
Sharpening

Topping

This is done when the saw teeth are at different heights or when the edge of the saw has worn unevenly and created a hollow. In order to top, a flat file is run on top of the teeth along the whole length of the blade until the tops of all the teeth are in one line.

Shaping

After topping, the teeth can then be cut to a uniform shape using a three-cornered saw file. The file should be held horizontally, at right angles to the saw.

Setting

The teeth are then set with the aid of a plier-type saw set. This has a plunger that pushes each tooth over by a pre-set amount. Care must be taken to ensure that the teeth are evenly set.

Sharpening

Lastly a three-cornered file is used to produce the cutting edge on the teeth. As cross-cut saws require knife-edge teeth, they should be filed at an angle of between 65 degrees and 75 degrees to the saw blade. The filing should be carried out in a direction towards the saw handle, keeping the file perfectly horizontal. Rip saw teeth must have chisel-end teeth. Therefore they are sharpened with the file held at right angles to the blade, keeping the file perfectly horizontal.

After sharpening, side-dressing should be carried out. This involves lightly rubbing a slipstone up and down the saw on both sides of the teeth to remove any burr caused by the filing.

Planes

Planes can be divided into two types:

Those used to produce a flat surface.
Those used to produce a rebate, plough groove, moulding or curve.

Cutting action and setting of planes

When planing timber, the thickness of the shaving and the smoothness of the finish is controlled by four factors:

1 The amount the cutting iron projects below the sole (bottom) of the plane. This can be adjusted in or out by turning the adjusting nut.
2 The distance the end of the back iron is set back from the end of the cutting iron. This should be set between 0.5 mm and 2 mm. The purpose of the back iron is:
To break the shavings.
To guide them out of plane.
To minimize tearing.
Note: Use a fine setting for finishing work and a coarser setting for rough planing.

3 The size of the mouth (the opening in the bottom of the plane through which the cutting iron projects) should be set only just wide enough to let the shavings pass through. A wide mouth tends to split the shavings away from the timber before it is cut by the blade.
4 Alignment of the cutting iron. The projection of the cutting iron through the mouth, must be parallel with the sole. If it is not, it may be corrected by moving the adjusting lever sideways.

Note: The cutting action of most planes is similar except that some have a tendency to tear the timber because of the absence of a back iron. This can be overcome to some extent by having a narrow mouth. Shoulder planes, block planes and others which are designed for fine cutting work, normally have a very narrow mouth and their cutting iron reversed, e.g. ground side uppermost. The grinding bevel on the cutting iron then acts as a back iron.

Flat-surface planes

Three main types are used for site or bench work. These are:

The jack plane
The try plane
The smoothing plane

All three have the same type of cutting unit, which consists of a cutting iron, back iron and lever cap. An exploded view of this type of plane is shown in Figure 10.

The *jack plane* is mainly used for reducing timber to the required size and for all rough planing work. Its length of 375 mm enables it to be used satisfactorily for straight planing. Being an all-round, general purpose plane it is ideal for both site and bench work.

The *try plane* is the largest plane a craftsman uses. Its main use is for straight planing and levelling. This type of plane varies from 450 mm to 600 mm in length.

The *smoothing plane* is a finishing plane. It is used for smoothing up a job after the jack plane has been used, and for general cleaning up work. Its length is 250 mm.

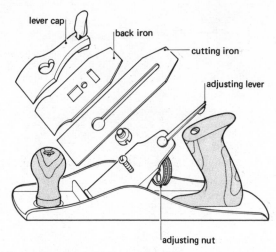

Figure 10   *Exploded view of a plane*

Special purpose planes

The main types available are:

Rebate
Side rebate
Plough
Multi-plane
Shoulder
Bullnose
Block
Router
Spokeshave

Note: All of these special purpose planes have one thing in common: they have only one iron, i.e. just a cutting iron and no back iron like the jack plane, etc.

The *rebate plane* (Figure 11) is used for cutting rebates up to 38 mm wide and 18 mm deep. This is normally carried out along the grain, but by using a spur, rebates may be cut across the grain. For larger rebates a bench rebate plane may be used.

The *side rebate* (Figure 12) is used for widening and cleaning up the sides of grooves, rebates and housings.

The *plough plane* (Figure 13) is used for cutting grooves along the grain and, with a spur, across the grain. A range of blades from 3 mm up to 16 mm are supplied with the plane.

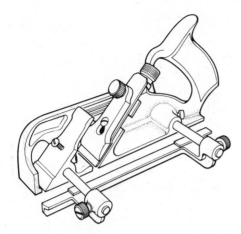

Figure 11   *Rebate plane*

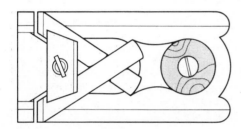

Figure 12   *Side rebate plane*

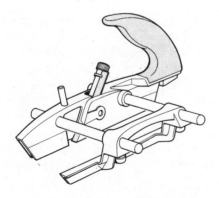

Figure 13   *Plough plane*

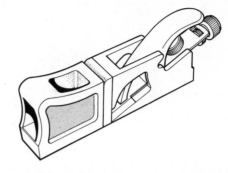

Figure 14   *Shoulder plane*

Figure 15   *Bullnose plane*

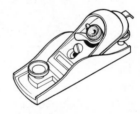

Figure 16   *Block plane*

The *multi-plane* combines the functions of both the rebate and plough planes. In addition it will also carry out various moulding operations. A full range of twenty-four blades are supplied with the plane. The multi-plane is similar in appearance to the plough plane.

The *shoulder plane* (Figure 14) is used for cleaning up and truing rebates and shoulders of joints.

The *bullnose plane* (Figure 15) is used for final working and cleaning up of stopped rebates and chamfers.

The *block plane* (Figure 16) is used for cleaning up and trimming end grain. Its length is 150 mm and it has a blade 42 mm wide.

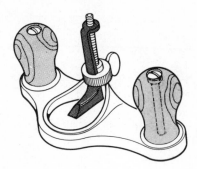

Figure 17   *Router plane*

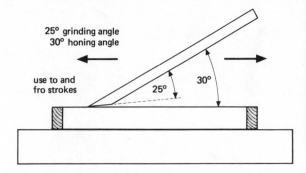

Figure 19   *Iron being honed on an oilstone*

Figure 18   *Spokeshave*

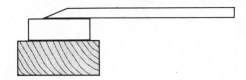

Figure 20   *Burr being removed from iron*

The *router plane* (Figure 17) is used to work and clean up housings. (The sides of the housing must be pre-cut with a tenon saw.)

The *spokeshave* (Figure 18) is used for the final working and cleaning up of curved edges. Two types are available:

Those with a flat bottom for convex shapes.
Those with a curved bottom for concave shapes.

The sharpening of cutting irons and chisels

Plane cutting irons and chisels are normally ground at an angle of 25 degrees and honed at an angle of 30 degrees. The sharpening of cutting irons and chisels is therefore a two-stage process.

Grinding which can be carried out on either:

A sandstone, which is a wet grinding process, water being used to keep the cutting iron cool and to prevent the stone becoming clogged.
A high speed carborundum grinding wheel, which is a dry grinding process, although to prevent the cutting iron overheating, it can be periodically cooled in water. If the tool is allowed to overheat it will lose its hardness.

Honing which is carried out on an oilstone. These normally have a fine and a coarse side. The fine side is for honing, the coarse side only being used when a grindstone is not available.

Procedure for sharpening
1   Grind iron, if required, on a grinding wheel (set tool rest to grind at an angle of 25 degrees).
2   Hone iron on the fine side of an oilstone which has been smeared with thin oil. (Use firm to and fro strokes keeping the cutting iron at a constant 30 degrees.) See Figure 19.
3   Remove burr from iron. (Use light strokes with the iron flat on the stone.) The iron can now be used. See Figure 20.
Note: It is not necessary to grind the cutting iron every time it is honed. Grinding before every third or fourth honing is considered adequate.

Shape of cutting edge
This depends on the work the plane has to do. See Figure 21. Both the try plane and the smoothing plane require a practically straight cutting edge. The jack plane iron often has a slightly round cutting edge so that it will work easily.
Note: The corners of the cutting iron for a smoothing plane are taken off to prevent them from digging in and ridging the surface.

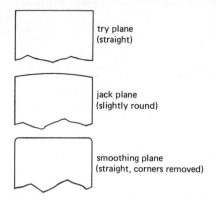

Figure 21   *Plane iron cutting edge*

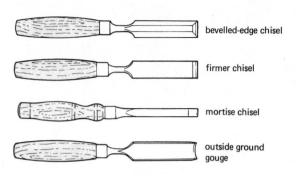

Figure 22   *Types of chisel*

Wood chisels

Chisels can be divided according to their use. See Figure 22.

Firmer
Mortise
Bevelled-edge
Paring
Gouges

Firmer chisels are general purpose chisels which can be used for all types of work. They are available in widths ranging from 3 mm to 50 mm. See Figure 22.

Mortise chisels are made much stronger than firmer chisels, in order to withstand the heavy blows from a wooden mallet and the levering necessary when chopping mortises. They are available in widths ranging from 3 mm to 25 mm. See Figure 22.

Bevelled-edge chisels are a lighter form of firmer chisel with bevels on the front edges of the blade. The thinner edges of this chisel enable it to be used for chiselling corners which are less than 90 degrees, such as dovetails etc. They are available in widths ranging from 3 mm to 50 mm. See Figure 22.

Paring chisels are similar to bevelled-edge chisels, but are much longer and lighter. They must be used for handwork only and never hit with a mallet. Their extra length makes them easier to control when paring either vertically or horizontally. They are available in various widths up to 50 mm.

Gouges are in fact curved chisels which are mainly used for shaping, scribing and carving. They are available in two types:

A scribing gouge is ground and honed on its inside curvature for paring and scribing concave surfaces.

A firmer gouge is ground and honed on its outside curvature for hollowing and carving.

Note: Gouges are sharpened according to their type. The scribing gouge is sharpened using a slipstone, and has its burr removed using a flat oilstone. The firmer gouge is sharpened on the flat oilstone and has its burr removed using a slipstone.

Boring tools

There are two types of drill used to bore holes:

Ratchet brace
Wheel brace

The ratchet brace and bits (Figure 23)
The ratchet brace is widely used for site work. The handle of the brace has a sweep of 125 mm. Sometimes it is necessary to bore holes in or near corners. In order to do this the ratchet on the brace is put into action. A wide range of bits are available for this type of brace. The main ones are:

The *jennings bit* (6 mm to 38 mm in diameter) can be used for boring both across the grain and into end grain.

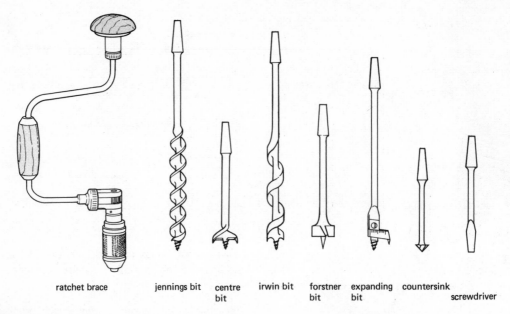

ratchet brace   jennings bit   centre   irwin bit   forstner   expanding   countersink
                                bit   bit   bit
                                                                              screwdriver

Figure 23   *Ratchet brace and bits*

The *centre bit* (6 mm to 32 mm in diameter) should only be used for boring shallow holes.

The *irwin bit* (6 mm to 38 mm in diameter) has the same range of uses as the jennings bit.

The *Forstner bit* (10 mm to 50 mm in diameter) is used for cutting blind or flat-bottomed holes.

Expanding bits (expands 13 mm to 75 mm) are mainly used for boring large holes.

Countersink bits are used to prepare holes in order to receive countersunk screws.

The *screwdriver bit* can be used as an alternative to the screwdriver. It also gives more leverage and has a quicker action.

The wheel brace and drill (Figure 24)

The wheel brace is used widely both on site and in the shop. Its main use is for boring pilot holes for screws etc. Twist drills are used in this type of brace. The drills are available in a range of sizes from 1 mm to 6 mm in diameter. A countersink bit is also available for the wheel brace.

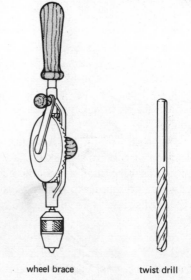

wheel brace   twist drill

Figure 24   *Wheel brace and drill*

Fixing tools

Fixing tools cover a wide range, but most either have a driving or turning action. The main types available are:

Hammers
Mallets
Screwdrivers
Pincers
Cold chisels
Plugging chisels
Nail punches
Bradawls

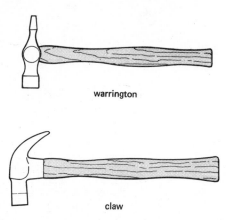

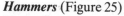

warrington

claw

Figure 25   *Hammers*

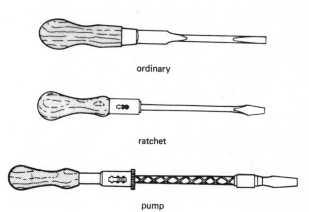

ordinary

ratchet

pump

Figure 27   *Screwdrivers*

Hammers (Figure 25)

Hammers are available in three main types for use by the carpenter and joiner.

The *warrington* or cross-pane hammer is used mainly by the joiner for shop work.

The *claw hammer* is a heavier hammer than the warrington. It is used mainly for site work.

The *pin hammer* is a light version of the warrington. It is used both on site and in the shop for driving small pins.

The handles of hammers are available in hickory, ash and steel. Hickory is the best wooden handle, but the steel-shafted hammer is often preferred for site work because it is stronger.

The mallet (Figure 26)

The mallet is mainly a joiner's tool which is used for driving chisels when cutting joints and for framing up. A suitable material for the head of a mallet is beech and the shaft is normally made from beech or ash.

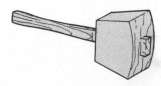

Figure 26   *Joiner's mallet*

Screwdrivers (Figure 27)

There are three main types of screwdriver used by the carpenter and joiner:

The ordinary screwdriver
The ratchet screwdriver
The pump screwdriver (or 'yankee')

All three types are available with ends suitable for use on slot-head or cross-head ('phillips') type screws.

The *ordinary screwdriver*. The one shown is known as a cabinet pattern screwdriver which is available in sizes (length of the blade) ranging from 50 mm to 300 mm.

The *ratchet screwdriver* is a handy tool as it allows screws to be turned in or removed without releasing the handle. It is available in a similar range of sizes to those of the cabinet screwdriver.

The *pump screwdriver* is popular with both carpenters and joiners as it allows quick and easy insertion and removal of screws. Also available for many pump screwdrivers are a range of interchangeable screwdriver bits, drill bits and countersinks.

Selecting a screwdriver

Always select a screwdriver that fits exactly into the head of the screw. Failure to do this will result in damage to the screwdriver and the head of the screw.

Pincers (Figure 28)

Pincers are used both on site and in the shop for removing small nails and pins. To avoid bruising the wood, joiners place a scraper or a thin block of timber under the levering jaw.

Figure 28   *Pincers*

Cold chisels (Figure 29)

These are steel chisels used for cutting holes or openings in brickwork, etc.

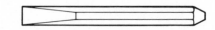

Figure 29   *Cold chisel*

Plugging chisels (Figure 30)

These are also steel chisels but they are exclusively used for raking out the mortar joints in brickwork to receive wooden plugs and joist hangers, etc.

Figure 30   *Plugging chisel*

Nail punches (Figure 31)

These are used to set nails below the surface of the timber. They are available in a wide range of sizes to suit most nails.

Figure 31   *Nail punch*

Bradawls (Figure 32)

Bradawls are used to form holes for nails and to give screws a start in softwood.

Note: Hardwood should be bored with a twist drill.

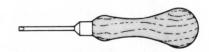

Figure 32   *Bradawl*

Marking-out tools

Marking-out tools consist of six main types:

Rules and tapes
Squares
Gauges
Marking knives
Trammel
Compasses

Rules and tapes

In general, carpenters prefer 1 m four-fold box-wood rules, and joiners prefer 600 mm steel rules. For longer measurements, both use steel tapes or pinch rods.

Squares

The *try square* (Figure 33) is used for setting out and checking right angles. It consists of two parts:

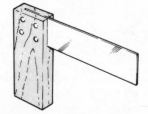

Figure 33   *Try square*

A steel blade, which is sometimes 'blued' to prevent it rusting
A rosewood stock

The squares are available with blade lengths varying from 100 mm to 300 mm.

The *mitre square* (Figure 34) is similar to the try square, but the blade and stock are set at an angle of 45° for marking out mitres. These are available with blade lengths between 200 mm and 300 mm.

The *combination square* (Figure 35) is a combination of the try and mitre square. The blade can be used as a 300 mm rule and often the stock is fitted with a small spirit level. The combination square is mostly preferred by carpenters for site work.

The *sliding bevel* (Figure 36) is an adjustable square which can be set to any angle and is used for marking out and testing angles, bevels and chamfers. It consists of a rosewood stock and a steel sliding blade which is normally fixed with a screw or wing nut. It is available with blade lengths varying from 150 mm and 300 mm.

Gauges

The *marking gauge* (Figure 37) is used for marking lines along the grain of a piece of timber parallel to a given surface, e.g. gauging or marking a piece of timber to the required width and thickness ready for planing. It comprises a stem with a pointed steel pin in one end to mark the timber, and a stock which is adjustable along the stem. It can be locked in the required position by turning the thumbscrew. Gauges are usually made from beech or rosewood and some types have small brass strips inlaid across the face of the stock to reduce wear.

The *mortise gauge* (Figure 38) is similar to the marking gauge and, as its name suggests, is used for marking out mortises. It has two pointed steel pins, one fixed and the other movable. This is so that the pins may be adjusted to the width of the required mortise.

The *cutting gauge* is again similar to the marking gauge, except that instead of a pointed steel pin it has a knife-shaped cutter. This gauge is mainly used for cutting across the grain of a piece of timber. It is also useful for cutting small quirks (rebates).

Marking knives (Figure 39)

These are used mainly for accurately marking shoulder lines before they are cut with a tenon saw. The knife should be used with its flat edge

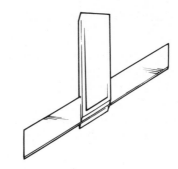

Figure 34　*Mitre square*

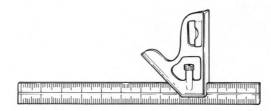

Figure 35　*Combination square*

Figure 36　*Sliding bevel*

Figure 37　*Marking gauge*

Figure 38　*Mortise gauge*

Figure 39　*Marking knife*

against the blade of a try square. Two types are available:

All steel with a knife edge on one end and on the other a scribing point.

A steel knife-end blade which is riveted to a wooden handle.

Note: Many joiners make their own marking knife from an old table knife.

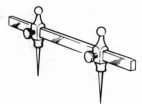

Figure 40   *Trammel*

Trammel (Figure 40)

This consists of a strip of timber on to which two steel trammel heads are clamped. It can be used as either a compass for drawing large curves and circles if a pencil is inserted into one of the heads, or dividers using the two steel points.

Scribing compasses (Figure 41)

These have two steel points and are used for marking a piece of timber when it has to fit up to an uneven or irregular surface, e.g. scribing skirting to fit an uneven floor.

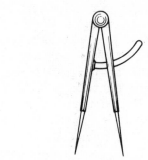

Figure 41   *Scribing compass*

Workshop equipment

A large number of items are required in order to produce a finished piece of work. The main range of equipment is:

Bench
Stools
Cramps
Bench equipment
Templates

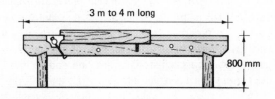

Figure 42   *Joiner's bench*

Bench (Figure 42)

The ideal joiner's bench should be 800 mm high, 3 to 4 metres in length and have a well or recess running down its centre so that tools may be placed in it without obstructing the bench surface. The bench should also have a bench stop, bench peg and a steel instantaneous-grip vice which opens at least 300 mm.

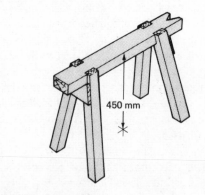

Figure 43   *Saw stool*

Saw stool (Figure 43)

Most carpenters and joiners require one or two sawing stools for their own use. These should be sturdily constructed with 50 × 50 mm legs, housed into a 75 × 100 mm top.

Cramps (Figure 44)

Three types of cramps are used in the workshop.

The *sash cramp* which is available in sizes from 500 mm to 2.0 m. This cramp is used to pull up joints, etc. when assembling and gluing up.

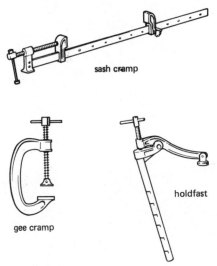

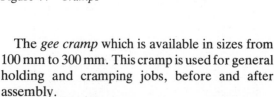

Figure 44   *Cramps*

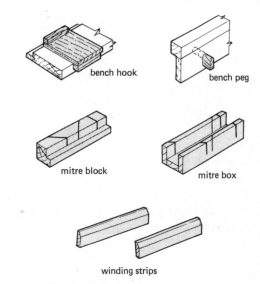

Figure 45   *Bench equipment*

The *gee cramp* which is available in sizes from 100 mm to 300 mm. This cramp is used for general holding and cramping jobs, before and after assembly.

The *holdfast* which is used for cramping jobs to the bench for sawing, cleaning up and finishing. The leg of the holdfast locates in a hole in the bench top.

Bench equipment (Figure 45)

Most joiners will make various items of wooden equipment for themselves. These may include the following items.

A *bench hook* which is used to steady small pieces of timber when cross-cutting, e.g. squaring ends, cutting to length and sawing shoulders.

Bench pegs which can be inserted in various positions along the side of the bench to support longboards, etc.

A *mitre block* which is used when cutting mitres for picture frames and other small mouldings.

A *mitre box* which is used when cutting mitres on larger mouldings such as architraves and skirtings.

Winding strips which are used to check timber and framed joinery items for wind or twist.

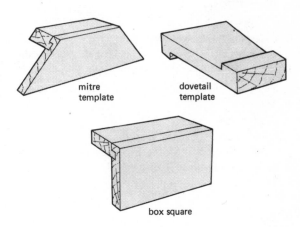

Figure 46   *Templates*

Templates (Figure 46)

Joiners often make up jigs and templates in order to make the job easier. Some of these are described below.

A *dovetail template* is used to mark out dovetails.

A *mitre template* is used to guide the chisel when mitring or scribing joints.

A *box square* is used to square lines around moulded sections.

Site equipment

The carpenter on site uses a range of equipment, some of which he makes himself. The main items of equipment are:

A stool
A mitre box
A straight edge
A plumb rule
Levels
A builder's square

Stool
The same size as a joiner's stool, this is used to support timber during sawing.

Mitre box
This is the same as a joiner's and is used for cutting mitres on skirtings and architraves.

Straight edge
This is used by many craftsmen including carpenters, bricklayers and plasterers. It is used in conjunction with a spirit level for lining, levelling and plumbing work. Figures 47 and 48 show the straight edge and level in use.

Plumb rule
This is made from a straight edge and a plumb bob and line and is used for plumbing and lining. It is very handy for door linings and grounds. Figure 49 shows a plumb rule in use.

Levels
There are two main types of level which the carpenter may use on site.

A *spirit level* is available in sizes from 230 mm up to 1.2 m. It is made from either aluminium or hardwood and is used for various plumbing and levelling work.

A *water level* consists of a length of hose with a glass or transparent plastic tube at each end. The water surfaces in the two tubes will give two level points. This uses the fact that water will always find its own level. It is used mainly to transfer levels around corners, etc. This is shown in Figure 50.

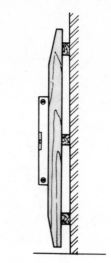

Figure 47   *Using a straight edge and level to plumb and line grounds*

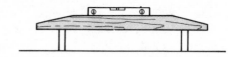

Figure 48   *Levelling two pegs, using a spirit level and straight edge*

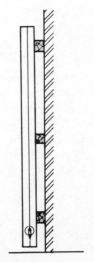

Figure 49   *Using a plumb rule to plumb and line grounds*

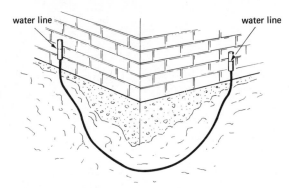

Figure 50   *Using a water level*

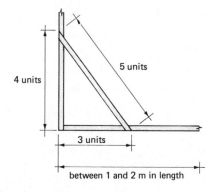

Figure 51   *Builder's square*

Builder's square (Figure 51)

This is mainly used for the setting out of a building. It should be made using the 3:4:5 rule, i.e. a triangle whose sides measure 3 units, 4 units and 5 units must be a right-angled triangle.

Miscellaneous items

There are a number of miscellaneous tools and items which a carpenter and joiner may have cause to use.

A *rasp* is a rough woodworker's file used for roughing out shaped work.

Various *metal-worker's files* are used for the maintenance of tools and adjusting metal fittings, etc.

A *scraper* is a rectangular piece of thin tool steel, 100×50 mm approximately. It is used for smoothing rough grain, particularly hardwoods, and also for cleaning up.

A *replaceable blade knife* to which various blades can be fitted enabling it to be used for cutting plasterboard, plastic laminate, building paper, roofing felt and insulation board, etc. It can also be fitted with a padsaw blade for cutting timber, or a hacksaw blade for cutting metal.

Self-assessment questions

1   Which of the following planes have more than one iron?
   (a)   rebate
   (b)   block
   (c)   jack
   (d)   shoulder

2   When squaring lines around a moulded piece of timber, the best tool to use would be a
   (a)   try square
   (b)   combination square
   (c)   mitre template
   (d)   box square

3   The purpose of a back iron in a plane is to
   (a)   make the cutting iron rigid
   (b)   secure the cutter
   (c)   break the shavings
   (d)   protect the cutting edge

4   Which saw would be the best to use for cutting down the sides of tenons?
   (a)   tenon saw
   (b)   rip saw
   (c)   panel saw
   (d)   bow saw

5   The plough groove shown in Figure 52 is found to be too tight for the panel. Which

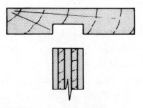

Figure 52   *Self-assessment question*

tool would be best to ease the sides of the groove?
(a) plough plane
(b) firmer chisel
(c) side rebate
(d) bench rebate

6 Which of the following is not a marking-out tool?
(a) mitre template
(b) mitre square
(c) try square
(d) combination square

Figure 53   *Self-assessment question*

7 What is the purpose of the item shown in Figure 53?
(a) chopping mortises
(b) plugging brickwork
(c) fitting mortise locks
(d) lifting floor boards

8 The honing angle for chisels and planes is
(a) 15 degrees
(b) 25 degrees
(c) 30 degrees
(d) 35 degrees

9 Rip saw teeth for cutting timber should be
(a) knife-pointed
(b) needle-pointed
(c) diamond-shaped
(d) chisel-shaped

10 In order to give screws a start, the best tool to use would be a
(a) jennings bit
(b) warrington hammer
(c) screwdriver
(d) bradawl

Answers to the self-assessment questions are given on page 142.

chapter 2

Woodworking machines and powered hand tools

After reading this chapter you should be able to:

1 Identify each of the following woodworking machines and state their main functions:
 (a) cross-cut saw
 (b) rip saw
 (c) dimension saw
 (d) surface planer
 (e) panel planer
 (f) band saw
 (g) mortiser
 (h) hand woodworking lathe

2 Recognize each of the following portable power tools and state their uses:
 (a) power drill
 (b) orbital and belt sanders
 (c) screwdriver

3 List general and individual safety precautions to be observed while using woodworking machines and portable power tools.

4 State the requirements of the Woodworking Machines Regulations 1974 applicable to each machine.

5 Select the correct machine or power tool for a given operation.

This chapter is not intended to enable the reader to use woodworking machines and portable power tools, but only to identify the various machines and power tools, along with their main uses and safe working procedures. It is most important before using *any* machine or power tool to be fully instructed in its use by your college lecturer or other competent person.

The use of all woodworking machines is governed by the Woodworking Machines Regulations 1974. It is the duty of every employer and employee, in places where woodworking machines are used, to ensure that they are aware of these regulations and that they are carried out in their entirety.

A copy of these regulations must be displayed wherever woodworking machine operations are carried out. It is essential that every woodworking machine operator and student has a thorough knowledge of these regulations and, in his own interests, fully implements them.

A copy of the Woodworking Machines Regulations 1974 is reproduced at the end of this chapter for reference purposes. The student is advised to study them as an integral part of this chapter.

Safety

Before using any machinery the operator should ask himself the following questions in the order they are given:

1 Have I been fully instructed in its use and am I capable of operating it?
2 Is the machine isolated from the power supply?
3 Is the machine and the working area around it clean and free from obstruction, offcuts and shavings, etc?
4 Are the cutters sharp and suitable for the work in hand?

5 Is the machine correctly set up?
6 Are all the guards and fences securely in place?
7 Are push sticks or a push block close to hand if required?

If the answer to any of the questions is no, rectify the position before continuing through the list.

The following general rules should be observed when using any machinery:

1 Never feed timber into a machine until the cutters have reached maximum speed.
2 Never make *any* adjustment to a machine while the cutter is moving.
   Note: Even after switching off, many machines take a considerable time to stop.
3 Never leave a machine until its cutter has stopped moving.
4 Never allow yourself to become distracted while operating a machine.
5 Never pass your hands over the cutters, even on top of the timber being machined.
6 Always isolate the machine and clean it down after use.

Cross-cut saw

The main purpose of the cross-cut saw is to cut the timber to approximately the required length. The range of work possible with a cross-cut saw is listed below:
Cross-cutting
Compound cutting
Cutting birdsmouths
Cutting housings
Cutting notches
Cutting halving joints
Kerfing
Ripping (with riving knife fitted)
Trenching, tenoning and ploughing with special cutters

Figure 54 shows a cross-cutting saw. The machine will cross-cut material up to 150 mm in depth and 610 mm in width. The saw can be adjusted to cut at any angle across the table. Compound angles can also be cut. Housings are

Figure 54   *Cross-cut saw*

cut by raising or lowering the table to the required depth.

The base of the machine is a prefabricated steel box section which must be firmly bolted to the floor in order to prevent any movement.

The motor is controlled by a recessed start button and a mushroom-head stop button. When connected up, all machines should also be fitted with an isolating switch. This is so that a machine can be completely isolated (disconnected) from the power supply when setting, adjusting, or carrying out maintenance work on the machine.

Note: The start button is recessed in order to prevent accidental switching on and the stop button is mushroomed to aid positive switching off. It should also be suitably located to enable the operator to switch the machine off with his knee in an emergency.

Unlike other circular saws, the material which is being cut remains stationary on the table, while the saw is drawn across it.

Rip saw

The main purpose of this machine is to resaw timber to the required section. This involves two operations:

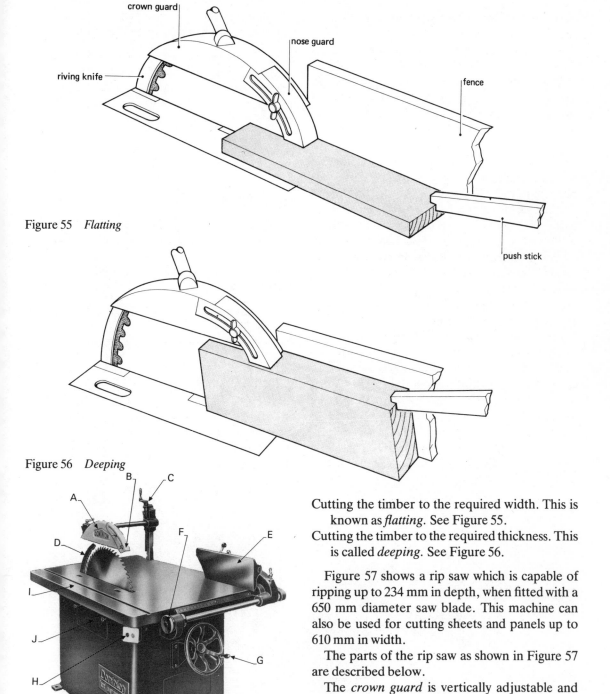

Figure 55   *Flatting*

Figure 56   *Deeping*

Figure 57   *Parts of the rip saw*

Cutting the timber to the required width. This is known as *flatting*. See Figure 55.

Cutting the timber to the required thickness. This is called *deeping*. See Figure 56.

Figure 57 shows a rip saw which is capable of ripping up to 234 mm in depth, when fitted with a 650 mm diameter saw blade. This machine can also be used for cutting sheets and panels up to 610 mm in width.

The parts of the rip saw as shown in Figure 57 are described below.

The *crown guard* is vertically adjustable and when set up for sawing, it must completely cover the gullets of the top teeth. (A)

The *nose guard* should be adjusted for each cutting operation so that the gap between the nose guard and the material being cut is as close as practicably possible. Approximately 10 mm is suitable. (B)

The *pillar* and adjusting handle for the crown guard. (C)

The *riving knife* rises and falls along with the saw when the depth of cut is altered. Whenever a saw blade is changed, the riving knife must be adjusted so that it is as close as practicably possible to the saw blade and, in any case, the distance between the riving knife and the teeth of the saw blade should not exceed 12 mm. The purpose of the riving knife is to stop the material binding on the saw blade while being cut and also to guard the back edge of the saw blade. (D)

The *fence* is adjusted by slackening the hand lever and moving the fence on its slide to the required position. (E)

Note: The fence should be set so that the arc at the end of the fence is in line with the gullets of the saw teeth at table level.

The *knulled adjusting knob,* by rotation, gives a fine adjustment of the fence. The measurement between the saw blade and fence is indicated on the graduated scale above the slide. (F)

The *rise and fall handle* raises or lowers the blade. (G)

Start and *stop* controls. (H)

The *table groove* enables a cross-cut guide or mitre fence to be used. (I)

The *access cover* is removed to give access to the spindle when changing saw blades. (J)

Note: Some saws have a recess on each side of the blade where it enters the table. These recesses are to receive felt packings and a hardwood mouthpiece. The packing helps to keep the saw cutting in a true line. The mouthpiece helps to prevent the underside of the timber breaking out or 'spelching'.

Dimension saw

This general purpose bench saw has a number of uses. It can be used for both cross-cutting and ripping operations to very fine tolerances. The range of work possible with a dimension saw is listed below:

Cross-cutting, ripping (flatting, deeping) and bevelling
Cutting compound bevels
Cutting sheet material

Figure 58 shows a dimension saw with a sliding table. It has a 130 mm depth of cut using a 450 mm blade. The parts of the dimension saw as shown in Figure 58 are described below.

The *sliding table* moves on rollers for cross-cutting and is locked in a fixed position for rip-

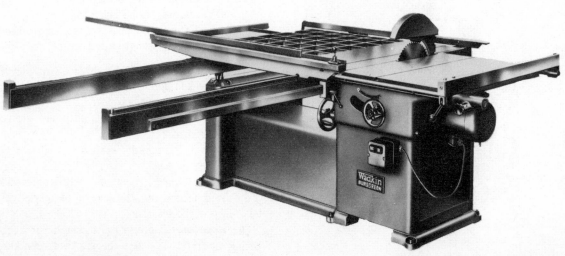

Figure 58   *Dimension saw*

ping. When changing the blade, the table can be moved to gain access to the saw spindle.

The *rip fence* is bolted on to the fixed saw table and can be removed when not required.

The *cross-cut fence* is bolted to the sliding table and can also be removed when not required.

The *riving knife* must be adjusted in the same way as for the rip saw.

The *crown guard* and *nose guard* must be adjusted in the same way as for the rip saw.

Start and *stop* controls.

The *brake* quickly stops the saw blade rotating. It also incorporates a switch which cuts off the power supply when the brake is applied.

The *rise* and *fall* handle.

The *saw cant handle* adjusts the angle of the saw blade from between 90 and 45 degrees enabling bevel cuts to be simply made.

Note: When using circular saws the operator's hand should not come closer than 300 mm from the saw blade. For the last 300 mm of the cut a push stick must be used. The push stick is also used for removing offcuts from the table around the blade. Figure 59 shows a typical push stick.

Blades

Figure 60 shows a section through a number of different circular saw blades. The main types and uses of these blades are as follows.

Hollow ground for dimension sawing and work to a fine section.

Swage for rip sawing thin section.

Ground off for rip sawing thin section.

Taper for rip sawing thin section.

Plate for straightforward rip and cross-cutting.

Note: The swage, ground off and taper saws are known as thin rim saws. Each has a particular range of applications but the purpose of all three is the same. This is to save timber by reducing the width of the saw kerf.

A part elevation of a number of circular saw blades is shown in Figure 61. The intended use for circular saw blades can be established by remembering the following basic rules.

Rip saws require teeth with chisel edges and the teeth must incline towards the wood. (They have positive hook.)

Note: Teeth for ripping hardwood require less hook than those for ripping softwood.

Cross-cut saws require needle-point teeth which incline away from the wood. (They have negative hook.)

Note: The needle-point teeth for hardwood cross-cutting must be strongly backed up.

Dimension sawing requires a blade with a combination of both rip and cross-cut teeth, though as dimension saw benches are rarely used for ripping, a fine cross-cut blade is often fitted.

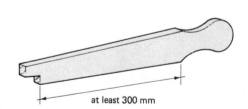

at least 300 mm

Figure 59   *Push stick*

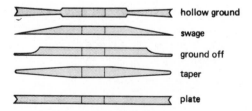

hollow ground
swage
ground off
taper
plate

Figure 60   *Circular saw blades (section)*

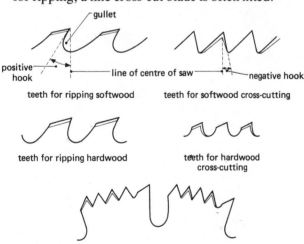

gullet

positive hook ————— line of centre of saw ————— negative hook

teeth for ripping softwood   teeth for softwood cross-cutting

teeth for ripping hardwood   teeth for hardwood cross-cutting

combination teeth for dimension saw

Figure 61   *Circular saw blades (part elevation)*

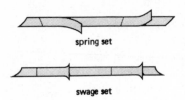

Figure 62   *Circular saw blades (set)*

The sharpening of circular saw blades is normally carried out on a saw-sharpening machine. The teeth can be set in two main ways as shown in Figure 62.

Spring set teeth where adjacent teeth are sprung to the opposite side of the blade.

Note: This is the same method as that used for hand saws.

Swage set teeth, mainly used for setting thin rim rip saws. The point of each tooth is spread out evenly on both sides to give it a dovetail-shaped look.

Surface planer

This machine has two main uses:

To produce a smooth, flat and straight face side on a piece of timber. This is called surfacing.

To produce a smooth, flat and straight face edge which is at right angles to the face side. This is called edging.

Note: This machine can also be used for bevel edging. This is carried out by fitting a pressure guard and canting the fence.

Figure 63 shows a surface planer which has a capacity to plane material up to 300 mm in width. The parts of the surface planer as shown in Figure 63 are described below.

The *infeed table* can be adjusted to vary the cutting depth, e.g. to vary the amount of timber which is to be planed off.(A)

The *outfeed table* should be level with the top of the cutting circle of the cutting block.(B)

The *bridge guard* guards the cutter block.(C)

The *fence* can be adjusted to any required position across the table and can also cant up to 45 degrees.(D)

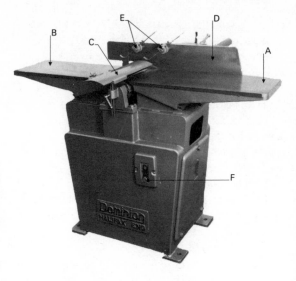

Figure 63   *Surface planer*

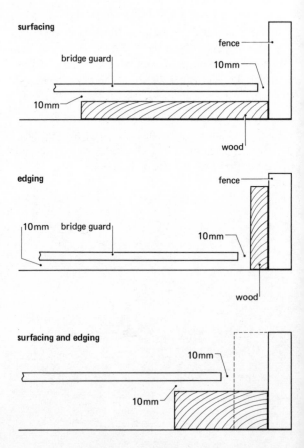

Figure 64   *Bridge guard positions*

Pressure springs are used when planing long lengths in order to keep the material in contact with the table.(E)

Start and *stop* controls.(F)

Figure 64 shows the various positions of the bridge guard when carrying out the following operations.

Surfacing

The bridge guard must be so adjusted that:

The gap between itself and the fence does not exceed 10 mm.

The gap between itself and the timber does not exceed 10 mm.

Edging

The bridge guard must be so adjusted that:

The gap between itself and the table does not exceed 10 mm.

The gap between itself and the timber does not exceed 10 mm.

Surfacing and edging

When carrying out these operations one after the other, the bridge guard may be adjusted so that:

The gap between itself and the timber when being surfaced does not exceed 10 mm.

The gap between itself and the timber when being edged does not exceed 10 mm.

Panel planer

This machine is also known as a thicknesser. Its purpose is to plane timber, which has previously been surfaced and edged to the required width and thickness. This is known as thicknessing.

Note: Combination machines are available which combine the function of both the surface planer and the panel planer. When using such a machine it is most important that the cutter block is adequately guarded while thicknessing.

Figure 65 shows a panel planer which has a capacity to thickness material up to 180 mm in depth. The maximum size timber this machine will accept is 180 × 300 mm. The parts of the panel planer as shown in Figure 65 are described below.

The *table* is adjustable up and down and has a pointer and graduated scale fixed to the side of it to indicate the various thicknesses of timber.(A)

The *rise and fall wheel* to adjust the table height controls the thickness of timber.(B)

The *gear change lever* controls the speed at which the timber is fed through the machine.(C)

The *cutter block guard* is hinged at one side to allow access to the cutter block.(D)

Start and *stop* controls.(E)

Figure 65   *Panel planer*

Figure 66   *Combination planer*

Figure 66 shows a combined surfacing and thicknessing machine. The features of both the surface planer and the panel planer are incorporated.

When planing timber to width and thickness on a panel or combined planer, the timber should be planed to width before being planed to thickness. This is so that the tendency for the timber to tip over in the machine is reduced to a minimum.

A push block used when surface planing short lengths of timber is shown in Figure 67.

The cutter block for a planing machine is usually circular and will normally contain two blades with the cutter block revolving at between 4000 and 6000 r.p.m. (revolutions per minute). A series of shallow cuts are made as the timber is fed over it. See Figure 68. This produces a ripple or cutter-marked finish on the timber surface. A slow feed speed produces a large number of cutter marks and therefore a smooth finish. A fast feed speed produces a small number of cutter marks which results in an irregular surface. An acceptable number of cutter marks per 25 mm for external joinery is between 10 and 25, and for internal joinery between 20 and 25.

Band saw

This saw, as its name implies, has a fairly long, endless narrow blade. Its main function is for cutting curves and general shaping work.

Figure 69 shows a band saw. The top and bottom casings have been opened to show the two 610 mm diameter wheels on which the band saw blade runs. Figure 70 shows the same band saw with these casings closed. The parts of the band saw as shown in Figure 70 are described below.

The *table* can cant up to 45 degrees to the right and up to 5 degrees to the left.(A)

The *fence* is removable when not required.(B)

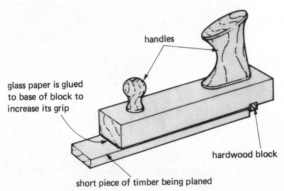

Figure 67   *Push block*

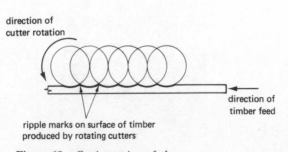

Figure 68   *Cutting action of planer*

Figure 69   *Band saw*

The *tension handle* raises or lowers the top wheel to adjust the tension of the blade.(C)

The *thrust wheel and guides* can be adjusted up or down to suit the thickness of the material being cut.(D)

Start and *stop* controls.(E)

The *brake*.(F)

Figure 71 shows a close-up view of the thrust wheel and guides above the table. There is also a similar arrangement below the table.

The purpose of the thrust wheel is to support the back of the blade and stop it from being pushed back during the cutting operation. These should be set up approximately 1 mm away from the back of the blade when it is stationary. The guides are set up to just clear the blade. Their purpose is to stop any sideways movement of the blade and keep it running true on its intended path.

Also shown is the hardwood mouth where the saw passes through the table.

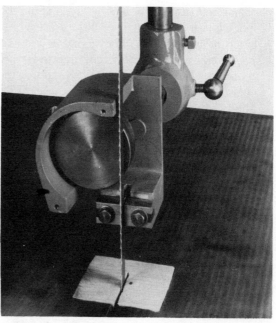

Figure 71   *Thrust wheel and guides*

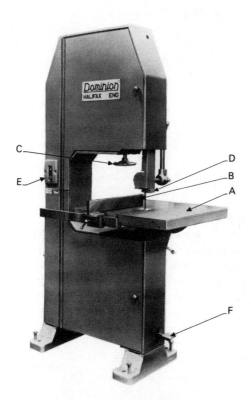

Figure 70   *Band saw with casings closed*

Various width band saw blades are available and in general the narrower the blade the tighter the curve that can be cut, i.e. widest blades for straight cuts and large sweeping curves, and the narrowest blades for small radius curves.

Mortisers

There are two main ways of machining mortises:

With a *hollow chisel mortiser,* the mortise is cut by a hollow chisel, inside which an auger bit rotates. The auger bit drills a round hole, thereby removing most of the waste, leaving the chisel to square up the hole. This cutting action is shown in Figure 72.

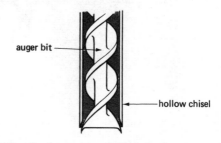

Figure 72   *Cutting action of chisel mortiser*

A *chain mortiser* is generally a combination machine which is capable of chisel mortising or chain mortising. The chisel mortiser is to be preferred where neatly cut mortises are required. But in production situations the chain mortiser is often used because of its ability to cut mortises at a much greater speed.

Hollow chisel mortiser

Figure 73 shows a hollow chisel mortiser which has a capacity to mortise timber with a section of up to 300 mm in depth and 200 mm in width. The parts of the machine as shown in Figure 73 are described below.

The *hand lever*. (A)

The *depth stop* stops the chisel at a predetermined depth, enabling mortises for stub tenons and haunching to be accurately cut. (B)

The *table*.(C)

The *grip vice* clamps the timber down on to the table and up against its back fence.(D)

The *cross-table traverse wheel* moves the table backwards and forwards so that the chisel may be aligned with the mortise.(E)

The *longitudinal traverse wheel* moves the table from side to side to enable the full length of mortise to be cut.(F)

The *chisel*.(G)

Start and *stop* controls.(H)

Various size chisels and bits are available, from 6 mm square up to 25 mm square. In order to accommodate this range of chisels and bits, different size collets must be fitted to both the chisel and bit to enable them to be tightened correctly. When correctly set up the bit should project 1 mm to 2 mm below the chisel. The machine edges of these chisels are sharpened by either a conical grinding stone which is fitted to some machines, or a steel reamer which is used in a carpenter's ratchet brace. Figure 74 shows both the conical grinding stone and steel reamer for sharpening hollow mortise chisels.

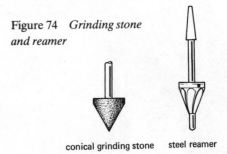

Figure 74   *Grinding stone and reamer*

conical grinding stone   steel reamer

Chain mortiser

Figure 75 shows a chain mortiser which has a capacity to mortise timber with a section of up to 300 mm in depth and 200 mm in width. The parts of the machine as shown in Figure 75 are as follows:

The *hand lever*.(A)

The *depth stop*.(B)

The *table*.(C)

The *grip vice*.(D)

The *cross table traverse wheel*.(E)

The *longitudinal traverse wheel*.(F)

The *chain*.(G)

Figure 73   *Chisel mortiser*

Figure 75   *Chain mortiser*

Figure 77   *Combination mortiser*

The *chain guard* is a hinged guard which covers the chain. The guard's action is automatic. As the chain cutter is lowered into the timber, the guard rests on the wood and as the chain cutter is lifted from the mortise, it is protected by the guard.(H)

The *grinding attachment* is an attachment for sharpening the cutting edges on the links of the chain.(I)

Note: The start and stop controls are not shown in Figure 75, but they are the same as on the machine shown in Figure 73.

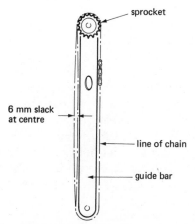

Figure 76   *Guide bar and sprocket*

Various size chains are available for this machine to cut mortises up to a maximum size of 32 mm wide and 75 mm long.

Figure 76 shows the guide bar and sprocket around which the chain runs. When the correct tension has been applied to the chain, it should have a 6 mm slack at its centre as shown.

Figure 77 shows a combined chain and chisel mortiser which incorporates the features of both the two previous machines. The start and stop controls on this machine work in conjunction with the hand levers which start the appropriate cutter when the lever is pulled downwards, and stop it when the lever is raised.

Hand woodworking lathe

The main purpose of this machine is the turning or shaping of wood into circular sections. This may be done in either one of two ways.

Along the grain, e.g. as with tool handles, turned chair and table legs and spindles, etc.
Across the grain, e.g. as with circular bowls and trays, etc.

Figure 78 shows a hand woodworking lathe which has a capacity between the centres to admit

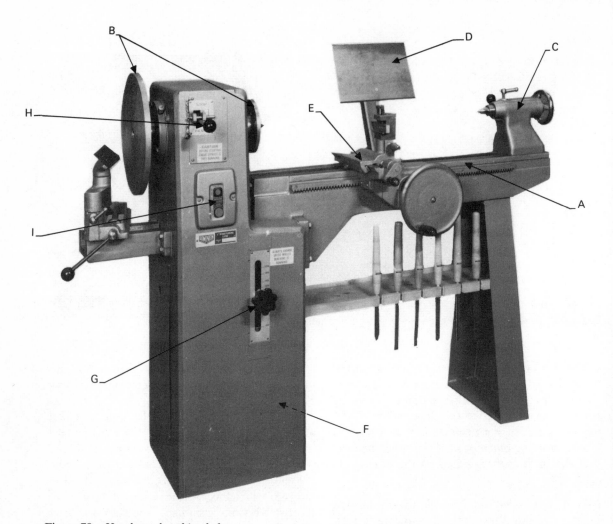

Figure 78   _Hand woodworking lathe_

timber up to 762 mm in length. The parts of the machine as shown in Figure 78 are described below.

The _bed._ (A)

The _headstock_ with inner and outer plates. (B)

The _tail stock._ (C)

The _drawing stand._ (D)

The _tool rest._ Another tool rest is also fitted when turning on the outside face plate. (E)

The _motor._ (F)

The _spindle speed adjuster._ The spindle speed is infinitely variable between 400 and 2200 r.p.m., the low speeds being used for heavy cutting, while the high speeds are used for finishing. (G)

The _brake,_ which operates a cut out switch. (H)

Start and _stop_ controls. (I)

Figure 79 shows a sanding table which has been fitted to a lathe. It is used in conjunction with a 300 mm sanding disc. The table can tilt at any angle up to 45 degrees and it carries a mitre fence for sanding compound-angled faces.

Figure 80 shows a lathe fitted with an attachment which enables deep holes of 8 mm or 11 mm diameter to be bored through the centre of the workpiece. Figure 81 shows a range of chisels for use on the lathe.

The _gouge_ is a round-nose hollow chisel used mainly for roughing cuts.

The *skew* is a vee-ground flat chisel with an angled end, used for smoothing cylinders, cutting shoulders and vee grooves.

The *spear* or *diamond-point* is a scraping tool used where it fits the contour of the work.

The *parting tool* is a double-ground chisel used for cutting off and making straight incisions.

The *round-nose* is a scraping tool used where it fits the contour of the work.

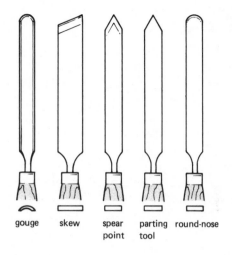

Figure 81   *Chisels for use on a lathe*

Figure 79   *Sanding table fitted to a lathe*

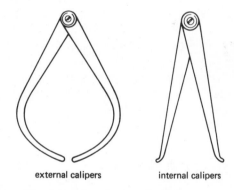

Figure 82   *Internal and external calipers*

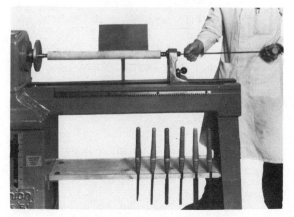

Figure 80   *Lathe with hole-boring attachment*

Figure 82 shows the internal and external calipers which are used for checking the inside and outside diameter of the work being turned.

Powered hand tools

The use made of portable power tools in the construction industry is ever-increasing. This results from the fact that industry is constantly trying to produce more at less cost, while at the same time still maintaining a high and safe standard of workmanship. This is especially true of the carpenter and joiner who has a wide range of powered hand tools at his disposal. These are:

Drill
Orbital sander
Belt sander
Screwdriver
Circular saw
Jig saw
Planer
Router
Ballistic tool

Note: The first four items are dealt with in this chapter, while the last five items are covered in *Carpentry and Joinery for Building Craft Students 2.*

Safety

When used correctly, powered hand tools are a useful aid to the carpenter and joiner and can save him both time and effort. When used incorrectly they are a source of potential danger, not only to the tool-user but also to any bystanders. This danger can result in serious injury, or in some cases even death.

Although each type of power tool has its own individual safe working procedures, the following basic safety rules should be followed when using any powered tool.

1   Never use a power tool unless you have been properly trained in its use.
2   Never use a power tool unless you have your supervisor's permission.
3   Always select the correct tool for the work in hand. (If in doubt consult the manufacturer's handbook.)
4   Ensure that the power supply is correct for the tool.
5   Ensure that the tool's cable is:
    a Free from knots and damage.
    b Firmly secured by the cord grips at both the plug and tool ends.
    c Unable to come into contact with the cutting edge or become fouled during the tool's operation.
    Note: This can be done by draping the cable over one shoulder during operation.
6   Before making *any* adjustments always remove the plug from the socket. Also ensure that the tool is switched off before replacing the plug in the socket.
7   Always use the tool's safety guards correctly and never remove or tie them back.
8   Never put a tool down until all rotating parts have stopped moving.
9   Always wear the correct protective equipment for the job. These may include:
    a Safety goggles
    b Dust masks
    c Ear protectors
    d Safety helmet
    Note: Loose clothing and long hair should be tied up so that they cannot be caught up in the tool.
10 All power tools should be properly maintained and serviced at regular intervals by a suitably trained person. Never attempt to service or repair a power tool yourself. If it is not working correctly or its safety is suspect, return it to the storeman with a note stating why it has been returned. In any case it should be returned to the stores for inspection at least once every seven days.
11 Ensure that the material or workpiece is firmly clamped or fixed in position so that it will not move during the tool's operation.
12 Never start or stop a tool under load. Always let it obtain its maximum speed before applying it to the job and remove it from the job before switching off.
13 Never use an electric tool where combustible liquids or gases are present.
14 Never carry, drag, or suspend a tool by its cable, as this causes loose connections and cable damage.
15 *Think* before and during use. Tools cannot be careless but their operators can. Most accidents are caused by simple carelessness.

Electrical safety

The power supply of a portable power tool can be either:

240 volts (mains supply)
110 volts (voltage reduced by a step-down transformer)

The 110 volt type is recommended for use on building sites, as the lower voltage reduces the effect of an electric shock, should a fault occur.

The power supply must be of correct voltage. This can be checked on the data plate which is fixed to the tool by the manufacturer. It is also recommended that it should not be possible to plug a tool into a socket of the wrong voltage. Therefore 110 volt plugs are coloured yellow and are of a different type to the 240 volt plugs.

Most power tools now available are manufactured using the double-insulated principle. This is a system, whereby the motor and other live parts are isolated from any section of the tool that it is possible for the operator to touch. In short, the inside is isolated from the outside. Double-insulated tools which bear the BS 2769 'Kitemark' and the double-squares symbol as shown in Figure 83 do not require an earth wire.

Figure 83

All other tools must be effectively earthed. They require a three core cable which is correctly wired up in accordance with the colour code. The cable of older tools may contain:

A *green* earth flex
A *red* live flex
A *black* neutral flex

Modern tools will have the new international colour-coded cable which consists of:

A *green*-and-*yellow* striped earth flex
A *brown* live flex
A *blue* neutral flex

Always remember to connect the flexes to the plug as follows:

1 Green or green and yellow flex to the terminal marked earth or E.
2 Red or brown flex to the terminal marked live or L.
3 Black or blue flex to the terminal marked neutral or N. See Figure 85 on page 40 and explanatory notes on page 41.

Note: If in doubt have the plug checked or wired by a competent electrician.

Where an extension cable is used, this should have a capacity at least equal to that which is fitted to the tool and when used for 110 volts, it should be connected to the output side of the transformer. Long trailing extension cables should be avoided as far as possible because of the ever-present danger of people tripping. In any case always position trailing cables with care.

The electric drill

This is probably the most used portable power tool. It is essential that the correct drill is selected for the work in hand. The following can be used as a general guide when selecting a drill:

A small hole requires a small high-speed drill.
A large hole requires a heavier duty, slower speed drill.
Drilling into concrete normally requires a drill incorporating a percussion device.

Figure 84 shows a small high-speed drill. This has a palm grip handle which ensures the pressure is exerted directly in line with the drill bit. The normal specifications and maximum drilling capacity for this type of drill is:

Figure 84 *High-speed drill*

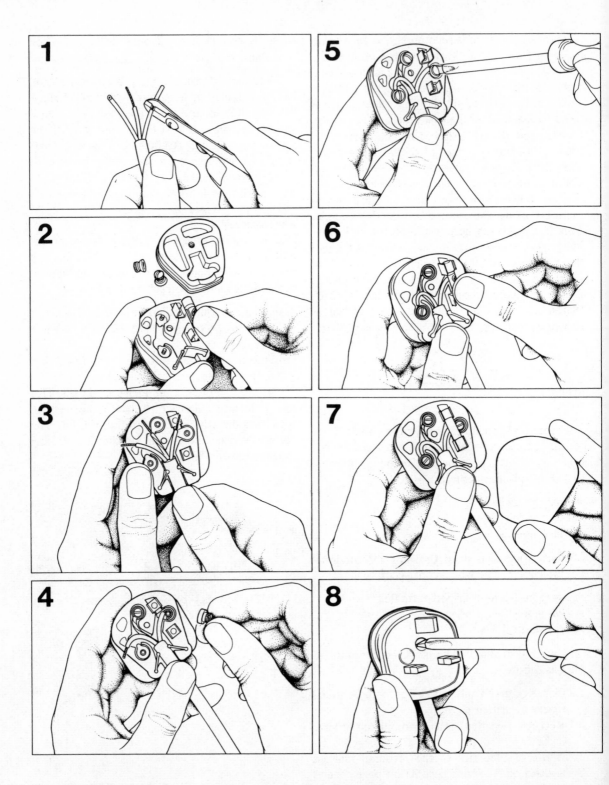

Figure 85   *Wiring a plug. Brown–live; blue–neutral; green/yellow–earth*

Weight	1.5 kg
Full load r.p.m.	1650
Watts	420

Maximum capacity for drilling into:

steel, up to	6 mm diameter
hardwood, up to	16 mm diameter
light alloy, up to	13 mm diameter
masonry, up to	10 mm diameter

Figure 86 shows a back handle, heavy-duty drill which is designed for two-handed operation. The normal specification and maximum drilling capacity for this type of drill is:

Weight	2.6 kg
Full load r.p.m.	590
Watts	500

Figure 86 *Heavy-duty drill*

---

1 Prepare the cable. The outer sheath should be stripped back 32 mm (1¼ in) and the insulation on the three cores should be removed to expose 15 mm (9/16 in) of conductor.

2 Prepare the plug. Remove the cover, take out the fuse and remove the terminal fixing nuts of the M K Safetyplug, or loosen the terminal screw in other makes of plug, to enable the conductor to be inserted. (The patented terminal nut used in the M K Safetyplug ensures a greater area of contact.)

3 Secure the cable in the cord grip. Note that the outer sheath should pass through the cord grip. It is essential that the cable is retained firmly in the cord grip, to prevent conductors being pulled out in service; the patented cord grip in the M K Safetyplug ensures a secure grip.

4 Connect the conductors: green/yellow to the Earth (centre) terminal; brown to the Live (right hand) terminal; and blue to the Neutral (left hand) terminal. Twist the conductors to ensure that there are no loose strands and wind them round the terminal pillar of the M K Safetyplug in a clockwise direction so that they are tightened as the fixing nut is screwed down.

5 Have a final check at the end to ensure that all the fixing nuts are securely tightened, and that there are no loose strands of wire.

6 Replace the (A S T A certified) fuse. For small appliances up to 700 W, for example table lamp, hair dryer, mixer/blender, sewing machine, hi-fi and television (black and white only), it is preferable to replace the brown 13 A fuse by a red 3 A fuse. Larger appliances that will need the 13 A fuse include deep freezer, refrigerator, electric fire, washing machine and colour T V.

7 Replace the cover, making sure that the conductors are within the appropriate wiring channels in the plug.

8 Tighten the captive cover fixing screw. (Part-insulation of the pins on the M K Safetyplug prevents risk of the plug pins being touched whilst the plug is being inserted or removed. They also prevent contact from knives and other implements inserted between the plug and socket-outlet by children.)

Maximum capacity for drilling into:

steel, up to	13 mm diameter
hardwood, up to	25 mm diameter
light alloy, up to	25 mm diameter
masonry, up to	25 mm diameter

Both the palm grip and the back handle drill are available in either single speed or two speed versions. When using two-speed drills, the higher speed should be used for drilling wood and the lower speed used when drilling metal and masonry.

Figure 87 shows a two-speed, back handle, rotary percussion drill. The normal specification and maximum drilling capacity for this type of drill is:

Weight	3.65 kg	
Full load r.p.m.	low speed	high speed
	680	1300
Full load percussive b.p.m. (blows per minute)	13.6	26
Watts	500	

Maximum drilling capacity in:

masonry, up to	38 mm diameter
concrete, up to	16 mm diameter

Note: The maximum masonry and concrete drilling capacities will vary according to the density and hardness of the material.

Twist drills and bits

Twist drills and bits used in electric drills should be of a high quality and able to withstand the heat which is generated when drilling at speed. The shank of the drill locates into the three jaws of the chuck. A chuck key is used to tighten the jaws of the chuck. This should be done in all three positions so that the jaws grip the shank of the drill evenly.

Note: Ensure that the chuck key is removed before starting the drill.

The main types of drill and bits used are shown in Figure 88.

Straight shank, twist drills are made from carbon or high-speed steel and are suitable for drilling both metal and wood. Drills made from high-speed steel are of a better quality.

A *countersink bit* of the type shown is suitable for countersinking holes to receive countersunk head screws, in both metal and wood.

Spade bits are used to drill large diameter holes in wood and other soft materials.

Figure 87 *Rotary percussion drill*

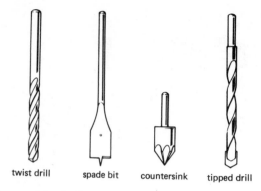

twist drill   spade bit   countersink   tipped drill

Figure 88   *Drills and bits*

Tungsten-carbide-tipped drills are similar to twist drills, but they have a tip of tungsten-carbide fitted into a slot in its cutting end. This type of drill is used for drilling masonry, ceramics and concrete.

Note: When using a tungsten-carbide-tipped drill in a percussion drill, ensure that the drill is recommended for this type of use by its manufacturers.

Sanders

Two types of sanders are used by the carpenter and joiner.

The orbital sander (Figure 89)

This type is also known as the finishing sander as it is mainly used for fine finishing work. The sander's base has a 3 mm orbit which operates at 12,000 r.p.m. Various grades of abrasive paper may be clipped to the sander's base. It is best to start off with a coarse grade to remove any high spots or roughness and follow on with finer grades until the required finish is obtained.

The orbital sander should be started and then brought into contact with the job. When the sanding is completed the sander should be removed from the job before the machine is stopped.

Note: Orbital sanding is most effective when the sander is moved over the surface using light up and down strokes. Do not put extra pressure on the sander as this will slow down the rate of sanding and overload the motor.

Figure 89   *Orbital sander*

Figure 90   *Belt sander*

The belt sander (Figure 90)

This is used for jobs requiring rapid stock removal. When fitted with the correct grade of abrasive belt they can be used for a wide range of operations such as smoothing and finishing joinery items, block flooring, and even the removal of old paint and varnish finishes.

The sanding or abrasive belt is fitted over two rollers. The front roller is spring-loaded and can be moved backwards and forwards by the belt-tensioning lever. This movement allows the belt to be changed easily and it also applies the correct tension to the belt. When changing the belt it is necessary to ensure that it will rotate in the correct direction. This is indicated on the inside of the belt by an arrow. If the belt is inadvertently put on the wrong way round, the lap joint which runs diagonally across the belt will tend to peel. This could result in the belt breaking with possible damage to the work surface. To keep the belt running central on the rollers there is a tracking control knob on the sander which adjusts the front roller by tilting it either to the left or right as required. The tracking is adjusted by turning the sander bottom upwards with the belt running and turning the tracking knob until the belt runs evenly in the centre without deviating to either side.

Operation of belt sander
Always start the sander before it is placed on the work surface and remove it from the work surface before switching the motor off. This is because slow-moving abrasive particles on the belt will deeply scratch the work surface. As with the orbital sander, the belt sander should be lightly guided over the surface with parallel overlapping strokes in line with the grain.

Note: Do not press down on the sander. The weight of the machine itself is sufficient pressure. Excessive pressure will cause the motor to overheat and the abrasive belt to become clogged.

Screwdrivers
When large numbers of screws have to be driven, the use of a power screwdriver will greatly speed up the process. Figure 91 shows a power screwdriver. The body and motor is similar to that of an electric power drill, although a reduction gear is fitted to give the correct speed for screwdriving. Where a two-speed tool is used, the slow speed should be used for wood screws and the high speed used for self-tapping screws.

The front housing of the tool holds the screwdriver bits and contains a clutch assembly. This operates in two stages:

The tool's motor will run but the screwdriver bit will not rotate until sufficient pressure is exerted to enable the clutch to operate and engage the main drive.

Figure 91   *Screwdriver*

When the screws are tight and in the required position, the second stage of the clutch operates and stops the screwdriver bit rotating.

The clutch can be adjusted by tightening or loosening the spring as required. If the adjustment is not suitable for the work in hand, the clutch spring can be changed for a weaker or stronger one. Four strengths are normally available. The weakest is used for driving smaller screws, or screws which are to be left proud of the surface, and the strongest for large or deeply driven screws. The two intermediate strength springs are used for a variety of operations in between these two extremes.

Various screwdriver bits are available to suit different types and sizes of screws. It is a simple operation to change the type of bit when required. The hexagonal shank of the bit is simply pushed into the front housing of the tool and retained in position by a spring-loaded steel ball which locates in a groove around the top of the shank. The bit is removed by simply pulling it out of the front housing.

Most tools are manufactured with a reverse gear to enable screws to be removed as well as inserted.

The Woodworking Machines Regulations 1974

Factories Act 1961
S.I. 1974 No. 903

The Secretary of State:

(*a*) in exercise of powers conferred by sections 17(3), 76 and 180(6) and (7) of the Factories Act 1961 (**a**) and now vested in him (**b**) and of all other powers enabling him in that behalf; and

(*b*) after publishing, pursuant to Schedule 4 to the said Act of 1961, notice of the proposal to make the Regulations and after the holding of an inquiry under that Schedule into objections made to the draft,

hereby makes the following Regulations of which all with the exception of Regulation 15 are special Regulations:

PART I

Applications, Interpretation and Exemptions

Citation, commencement, revocation and amendment

1 (1) These Regulations may be cited as the Woodworking Machines Regulations 1974 and shall come into operation on 24th November 1974 with the exception of Regulation 41 which shall come into operation on 24th May 1976.

(2) The Regulations specified in columns 1 and 2 of Schedule 2 to these Regulations are hereby revoked to the extent respectively specified in relation thereto in column 3 of that Schedule.

(3) Regulation 67(2) of the Shipbuilding and Ship-repairing Regulations 1960(**c**) and Regulation 42 of the Construction (General Provisions) Regulations 1961(**d**) shall not apply to the parts of woodworking machines required by these Regulations to be guarded or to have other safeguards.

Interpretation

2 (1) The Interpretation Act 1889(**e**) shall apply to the interpretation of these Regulations as it applies to the interpretation of an Act of Parliament, and as if these Regulations and the Regulations hereby revoked were Acts of Parliament.

(2) In these Regulations, unless the context otherwise requires, the following expressions have the meanings hereby assigned to them respectively, that is to say:

"approved" means approved for the time being for the purposes of these Regulations by certificate of the Chief Inspector;

"circular sawing machine" means a sawing machine comprising a saw bench (including a bench in the form of a roller table and a bench incorporating a travelling table) with a spindle situated below the machine table to which a circular saw blade can be fitted for the purpose of dividing material into separate parts, but does not include a multiple rip sawing machine, a straight line edging machine or any sawing machine in the operation of which the blade is moved towards the material which is being cut;

"cutters" include saw blades, chain cutters, knives, boring tools, detachable cutters and solid cutters;

"factory" includes any place to which these Regulations apply;

"machine table" includes, in relation to a circular sawing machine, any frame which supports the material being cut;

"narrow band sawing machine" means a sawing machine designed to be fitted with a blade not exceeding 50 millimetres in width in the form of a continuous band or strip the cutting portion of which runs in a vertical direction, but does not include a log band sawing machine or a band resawing machine;

"planing machine" means a machine for surfacing or for thicknessing or a combined machine for both those operations but does not include a multicutter moulding machine having two or more cutter spindles;

"principal Act" means the Factories Act 1961 as amended by or under any other Act;

"sawmill" means premises which are used

(a) 1961 c.34.
(b) S.I. 1968/729 (1968 II, p. 2108).
(c) S.I. 1960/1932 (1960 II, p. 1427).
(d) S.I. 1961/1580 (1961 II, p. 3207).
(e) 1889 c. 63.
(f) S. R. & O. 1941/94 (Rev. VII, p. III: 1941 I, p. 280).

solely or mainly for the purpose of sawing logs (including square logs) into planks or boards;

"squared stock" means material having a rectangular (including square) cross section of which the dimensions remain substantially constant throughout the length of the material;

"surfacing" means the planing or smoothing of the surface of material by passing it over cutters and includes chamfering and bevelling, but does not include moulding, tenoning, rebating or recessing;

"vertical spindle moulding machine" includes a high-speed routing machine; and

"woodworking machine" means any machine (including a portable machine) of a kind specified in Schedule 1 to these Regulations for use on all or any one or more of the following, that is to say, wood, cork and fibre board and material composed partly of any of those materials.

Application and operation of Regulations

3 (1) These Regulations, other than Regulation 15 (which relates to the sale or hire of machinery), shall apply to any of the following, in which any woodworking machine is used, that is to say, to factories and to any premises, places, processes, operations and works to which the provisions of Part IV of the principal Act with respect to special regulations for safety and health are applied by any of the following provisions of that Act, namely, section 123 (which relates to electrical stations), section 124 (which relates to institutions), section 125 (which relates to certain dock premises and certain warehouses), section 126 (which relates to ships) and section 127 (which relates to building operations and works of engineering construction).

(2) In relation to the parts of woodworking machines required by these Regulations to be guarded or to have other safeguards, the provisions of these Regulations as respects guarding and the provision of other safeguards are in substitution for the provisions of section 14(1) of the principal Act and accordingly the provisions of that subsection shall not apply in relation to any such parts.

(3) The provisions of Regulation 12 are in substitution for section 3(1) of the principal Act and accordingly the provisions of that subsection shall not apply in relation to any room to which that Regulation applies.

(4) Except as provided in paragraphs (2) and (3) of this Regulation, the provisions of these Regulations shall be in addition to and not in substitution for the provisions of the principal Act.

Exemptions

4 The Chief Inspector may (subject to such conditions, if any, as may be specified therein) by certificate in writing (which he may in his discretion revoke at any time) exempt from all or any of the requirements of these Regulations:

(*a*) any particular woodworking machine or any type of woodworking machine; or

(*b*) any operation or process or any class or description of operations or processes; or

(*c*) any factory or any part of any factory or any class or description of factories or parts thereof,

if he is satisfied that the requirements in respect of which the exemption is granted are not necessary for the protection of persons employed. Where such exemption is granted, a legible copy of the certificate, showing the conditions (if any) subject to which it has been granted, shall be kept posted in any factory in which the exemption applies in a position where it may be conveniently read by the persons employed.

PART II

All Woodworking Machines – General

Provision and construction of guards

5 (1) Without prejudice to the other provisions of these Regulations, the cutters of every woodworking machine shall be enclosed by a guard or guards to the greatest extent that is practicable having regard to the work being done thereat, unless the cutters are in such position as to be as safe to every person employed as they would be if so enclosed.

(2) All guards provided in pursuance of the foregoing paragraph of this Regulation shall be of substantial construction.

Adjustment of machines and guards

6 No person shall, while the cutters are in motion:

(*a*) make any adjustment to any guard on a woodworking machine unless means are provided whereby such an adjustment can be made without danger; or

(*b*) make any adjustment to any part of a woodworking machine, except where the adjustment can be made without danger.

Use and maintenance of guards, etc.

7 (1) At all times while the cutters are in motion, the guard and devices required by these Regulations and all such safeguards as are mentioned in Regulation 8 shall be kept constantly in position and properly secured and adjusted except when, and to the extent to which, because of the nature of the work being done, the use of any such guard, device, or safeguard is rendered impracticable:

Provided that the said exception shall not apply to the use of any guard required by Regulations 18(1), 21(1) or (2), 22(1), 23, 28, 30 or 31.

(2) The said guards, devices, and safeguards, and all such appliances as are mentioned in Regulation 14(1)(*b*) shall be properly maintained.

Exception from obligations to provide guards, etc.

8 Regulations 5, 16, 21, 22, 26, 28, 30, 31 and 36 shall not apply to any machine in respect of which other safeguards are provided which render the machine as safe as it would be if the provisions of those Regulations were complied with.

Machine controls

9 Every woodworking machine shall be provided with an efficient device or efficient devices for starting and stopping the machine and the control or controls of the device or devices shall be in such a position and of such design and construction as to be readily and conveniently operated by the person operating the machine.

Working space

10 There shall be provided around every woodworking machine sufficient clear and unobstructed space to enable, in so far as is thereby practicable, the work being done at the machine to be done without risk of injury to persons employed.

Floors

11 The floor or surface of the ground around every woodworking machine shall be maintained in good and level condition and, as far as reasonably practicable, free from chips and other loose material and shall not be allowed to become slippery.

Temperature

12 (1) Subject to the following provisions of this Regulation, effective provision shall be made for securing and maintaining a reasonable temperature in every room or other place (not in the open air) in which a woodworking machine is being worked.

(2) In that part of any room or other place (not in the open air) in which a woodworking machine is being worked, a temperature of less than 13 degrees Celsius shall not be deemed at any time to be a reasonable temperature except where and in so far as the necessities of the business carried on make it impracticable to maintain a temperature of at least 13 degrees Celsius.

(3) Where it is impracticable for the aforesaid reasons to maintain a temperature of at least 13 degrees Celsius in any such part of a room or place as aforesaid, there shall be provided in the said part, to the extent that is reasonably practicable, effective means of warming persons working there.

(4) There shall not be used in any such room or place as aforesaid any heating appliance other than an appliance in which the heating element or flame is so enclosed within the body of the appliance that there is no likelihood of the accidental ignition of any material in that room or place by reason of contact with or proximity to the heating element or any flame, except where the heating appliance is so positioned or protected that there is no such likelihood.

(5) Paragraphs (2) and (3) of this Regulation shall in their application to parts of factories which are used as sawmills have effect as if for the references to 13 degrees Celsius there were substituted references to 10 degrees Celsius.

(6) No method of heating shall be employed which results in the escape into the air of any such room or place as aforesaid of any fume of such a character and to such extent as to be likely to be injurious or offensive to persons employed therein.

Training

13 (1) No person shall be employed on any kind of work at a woodworking machine unless:

(*a*) he has been sufficiently trained at machines of a class to which that machine belongs in the kind of work on which he is to be employed; and

(*b*) he has been sufficiently instructed in accordance with paragraph (2) of this Regulation,

except where he works under the adequate supervision of a person who has a thorough knowledge and experience of the working of the machine and of the matters specified in paragraph (2) of this Regulation.

(2) Every person, while being trained to work at a woodworking machine, shall be fully and carefully instructed as to the dangers arising in connection with such machine, the precautions to be observed, the requirements of these Regulations which apply and, in the case of a person being trained to operate a woodworking machine, the method of using the guards, devices and appliances required by these Regulations.

(3) Without prejudice to the foregoing provisions of this Regulation, a person who has not attained the age of 18 years shall not operate any circular sawing machine, any sawing machine fitted with a circular blade, any planing machine for surfacing which is not mechanically fed, or any vertical spindle moulding machine, unless he has successfully completed an approved course of training in the operation of such a machine. Save that where required to do so as part of such a course of training, he may operate such a machine under the adequate supervision of a person who has a thorough knowledge and experience of the working of the machine and of the matters specified in paragraph (2) of this Regulation.

Duties of persons employed

14 (1) Every person employed shall, while he is operating a woodworking machine:

(*a*) use and keep in proper adjustment the guards and devices provided in accordance with these Regulations and all such safeguards as are mentioned in Regulation 8; and

(*b*) use the spikes, push-sticks, push-blocks, jigs, holders and back stops provided in accordance with these Regulations,

except (in cases other than those specified in the proviso to Regulation 7(1)) when, because of the nature of the work being done, the use of the said guards, devices or other safeguards, or of the appliances mentioned in sub-paragraph (*b*) of this paragraph, is rendered impracticable.

(2) It shall be the duty of every person, being a person employed by the occupier of a factory and trained in accordance with Regulation 13, who discovers any defect in any woodworking machine in that factory or in any guard, device or appliance provided in accordance with these Regulations or in any such safeguard as is mentioned in Regulation 8 (being a defect which may affect the safe working of a woodworking machine) or who discovers that the floor or surface of the ground around any woodworking machine in that factory is not in good and level condition or is slippery, to report the matter without delay to the occupier, manager or other appropriate person.

Sale or hire of machinery

15 The provisions of section 17(2) of the principal Act (which prohibits the sale or letting on hire of certain machines which do not comply with the requirements of that section) shall extend to any woodworking machine which is for use in a factory and which is not provided with such guards or devices as are necessary, and is not so designed and constructed as, to enable any requirement of the following Regulations to be complied with, that is to say, Regulations 9, 16, 17(3), 21, 22, 24, 25, 26, 27, 28, 30, 31 and 39 in so far as the requirement applies to that woodworking machine.

PART III

Circular Sawing Machines

Guarding of circular sawing machines

16 (1) That part of the saw blade of every circular sawing machine which is below the machine table shall be guarded to the greatest extent that is practicable.

(2) There shall be provided for every circular sawing machine a riving knife which shall be securely fixed by means of a suitable device situated below the machine table, be behind and in a direct line with the saw blade, have a smooth surface, be strong, rigid and easily adjustable and fulfil the following conditions:

(*a*) the edge of the knife nearer the saw blade shall form an arc of a circle having a radius not exceeding the radius of the largest saw blade with which the saw bench is designed to be used;

(*b*) the knife shall be capable of being so adjusted and shall be kept so adjusted that it is as close as practicable to the saw blade, having regard to the nature of the work being done, and so that at the level of the machine table the distance between the edge of the knife nearer to the saw blade and the teeth of the saw blade does not exceed 12 millimetres;

(*c*) for a saw blade of a diameter of less than 600 millimetres, the knife shall extend upwards from the machine table to a height above the machine table which is not more than 25 millimetres below the highest point of the saw blade, and for a saw blade of a diameter of 600 millimetres or over, the knife shall extend upwards from the machine table to a height of at least 225 millimetres above the machine table; and

(*d*) in the case of a parallel plate saw blade the knife shall be thicker than the plate of the saw blade.

(3) Without prejudice to the requirements of Regulation 18(1), that part of the saw blade of every circular sawing macine which is above the machine table shall be guarded with a strong and easily adjustable guard, which shall be capable of being so adjusted and shall be kept so adjusted that it extends from the top of the riving knife to a point above the upper surface of the material being cut which is as close as practicable to that surface or, where squared stock is being fed to the saw blade by hand, to a point which is not more than 12 millimetres above the upper surface of the material being cut.

(4) The guard referred to in the last foregoing paragraph shall have a flange of adequate depth on each side of the saw blade and the said guard shall be kept so adjusted that the said flanges extend beyond the roots of the teeth of the saw blade. Where the guard is fitted with an adjustable front extension piece, that extension piece shall have along the whole of its length a flange of adequate depth on the side remote from the fence and the said extension piece shall be kept so adjusted that the flange extends beyond the roots of the teeth of the saw blade:

Provided that in the case of circular sawing machines manufactured before the date of the coming into operation of this Regulation, the requirements of this paragraph shall not apply until two years after the said date and in the case of such machines, until the expiration of the said period, the said guard shall have along the whole of its length a flange of adequate depth on the side remote from the fence and shall be kept so adjusted that the said flange extends beyond the roots of the teeth of the saw blade.

Sizes of circular saw blades

17 (1) In the case of a circular sawing machine the spindle of which is not capable of being operated at more than one working speed, no saw blade shall be used thereat for dividing material into separate parts which has a diameter of less than six-tenths of the diameter of the largest saw blade with which the saw bench is designed to be used.

(2) In the case of a circular sawing machine which has arrangements for the spindle to operate at more than one working speed, no saw blade shall be used thereat for dividing material into separate parts which has a diameter of less than six-tenths of the diameter of the largest saw blade which can properly be used at the fastest working speed of the spindle at that saw bench.

(3) There shall be securely affixed to every circular sawing machine a notice specifying the diameter of the smallest saw blade which may be used in the machine in compliance with paragraph (1) or (2) (as the case may be) of this Regulation.

Limitations on use of circular sawing machines for certain purposes

18 (1) No circular sawing machine shall be used for cutting any rebate, tenon, mould or groove, unless that part of the saw blade or other cutter which is above the machine table is effectively guarded.

(2) No circular sawing machine shall be used for a ripping operation (other than any such operation involved in cutting a rebate, tenon, mould or groove) unless the teeth of the saw blade project throughout the operation through the upper surface of the material being cut.

(3) No circular sawing machine shall be used for cross-cutting logs or branches unless the material being cut is firmly held by a gripping device securely fixed to a travelling table.

Provision of push-sticks

19 (1) A suitable push-stick shall be provided and kept available for use at every circular sawing machine which is fed by hand.

(2) Except where the distance between a circular saw blade and its fence is so great or the method of feeding material to the saw blade is such that the use of a push-stick can safely be dispensed with, the push-stick so provided shall be used:

(*a*) to exert feeding pressure on the material between the saw blade and the fence throughout any cut of 300 millimetres or less in length;

(*b*) to exert feeding pressure on the material between the saw blade and the fence during the last 300 millimetres of any cut of more than 300 millimetres in length; and

(*c*) to remove from between the saw blade and the fence pieces of material which have been cut.

Removal of material cut by circular sawing machines

20 (1) Except as provided in paragraph (3) of this Regulation, where any person (other than the operator) is employed at a circular sawing machine in removing while the saw blade is in motion material which has been cut, that person shall not for that purpose stand elsewhere than at the delivery end of the machine.

(2) Except as provided in paragraph (3) of this Regulation, where any person (other than the operator) is employed at a circular sawing machine in removing while the saw blade is in motion material which has been cut, the machine table shall be constructed or shall be extended over its whole width (by the provision of rollers or otherwise) so that the distance between the delivery end of the table or of any such extension thereof and the up-running part of the saw blade is not less than 1200 millimetres. Provided that this requirement shall not apply to moveable machines which cannot accommodate a blade having a diameter of more than 450 millimetres.

(3) The requirements of paragraphs (1) and (2) of this Regulation shall not apply to a circular sawing machine having a saw bench in the form of a roller table or a saw bench incorporating a travelling table which (in either case) is in motion during the cutting operation.

PART IV

Multiple Rip Sawing Machines and Straight Line Edging Machines

21 (1) Every multiple rip sawing machine and straight line edging machine shall be provided on the operator's side of the in-feed pressure rollers with a suitable device which shall be of such design and so constructed as to contain so far as practicable any material accidentally ejected by the machine and every such device shall extend for not less than the full width of the said pressure rollers.

(2) Every multiple rip sawing machine and straight line edging machine on which the saw spindle is mounted above the machine table shall, in addition to the device required to be provided under paragraph (1) of this Regulation, be fitted on the side remote from the fence with a suitable guard, which shall extend from the edge of the said device along a line parallel to the blade of the saw at least 300 millimetres towards the axis of the saw and shall be of such a design and so constructed as

to contain as far as practicable any material accidentally ejected from the machine.

(3) In the case of multiple rip sawing machines and straight line edging machines manufactured before the date of the coming into operation of this Regulation, the requirements of this Regulation shall not apply until two years after the said date.

PART V

Narrow Band Sawing Machines

22 (1) The saw wheels of every narrow band sawing machine and the whole of the blade of every such machine, except that part of the blade which runs downwards between the top wheel and the machine table, shall be enclosed by a guard or guards of substantial construction.

(2) That part of the blade of every such machine as aforesaid which is above the friction disc or rollers and below the top wheel shall be guarded by a frontal plate which is as close as is practicable to the saw blade and has at least one flange at right angles to the plate and extending behind the saw blade.

(3) The friction disc or rollers of every such machine as aforesaid shall be kept so adjusted that they are as close to the surface of the machine table as is practicable having regard to the nature of the work being done.

PART VI

Planing Machines

Limitation on use of planing machines
23 No planing machine shall be used for cutting any rebate, recess, tenon or mould unless the cutter is effectively guarded.

Cutter blocks for planing machines for surfacing
24 Every planing machine for surfacing which is not mechanically fed shall be fitted with a cylindrical cutter block.

Table gap
25 (1) Every planing machine for surfacing which is not mechanically fed shall be so designed and constructed as to be capable of adjustment so

that the clearance between the cutters and the front edge of the delivery table does not exceed 6 millimetres (measured radially from the centre of the cutter block) and the gap between the feed table and the delivery table is as small as practicable having regard to the operation being performed, and no such planing machine which is not so adjusted shall be used for surfacing.

(2) In the case of planing machines manufactured before the date of the coming into operation of this Regulation, the requirements of the foregoing paragraph of this Regulation shall not apply until twelve months after the said date.

Provision of bridge guards
26 (1) Every planing machine for surfacing which is not mechanically fed shall be provided with a bridge guard which shall be strong and rigid, have a length not less than the full length of the cutter block and a width not less than the diameter of the cutter block and be so constructed as to be capable of easy adjustment both in a vertical and horizontal direction.

(2) Every bridge guard provided in pursuance of paragraph (1) of this Regulation shall be mounted on the machine in a position which is approximately central over the axis of the cutter block and shall be so constructed as to prevent its being accidentally displaced from that position.

(3) In the case of planing machines manufactured before the date of the coming into operation of this Regulation, the requirements of this Regulation shall not apply until twelve months after the said date, and until the expiration of the said period such machines for surfacing shall be provided with a bridge guard capable of covering the full length and breadth of the cutting slot in the bench and so constructed as to be easily adjusted both in a vertical and horizontal direction.

Adjustment of bridge guards
27 (1) While a planing machine which is not mechanically fed is being used for surfacing, the bridge guard provided in pursuance of Regulation 26 shall be so adjusted as to enable, so far as is thereby practicable, the work being done at the machine to be done without risk of injury to persons employed.

(2) Except as provided in paragraph (4) of this Regulation and in Regulation 29, when a wider surface of squared stock is being planed or smoothed, the bridge guard so provided shall be adjusted so that the distance between the end of the guard and the fence does not exceed 10 millimetres and the underside of the guard is not more than 10 millimetres above the upper surface of the material.

(3) Except as provided in paragraph (4) of this Regulation, when a narrower surface of squared stock is being planed or smoothed, the bridge guard so provided shall be adjusted so that the end of the guard is at a point not more than 10 millimetres from the surface of the said material which is remote from the fence and the underside of the guard is not more than 10 millimetres above the surface of the feed table.

(4) When the planing or smoothing both of a wider and of a narrower surface of squared stock is being carried out, one operation immediately following the other, the bridge guard so provided shall be adjusted so that when a wider surface is being planed or smoothed the underside of the guard is not more than 10 millimetres above the upper surface of the material and, when a narrower surface is being planed or smoothed, the end of the guard is at a point not more than 10 millimetres from the surface of the said material which is remote from the fence.

(5) Except as provided in paragraph (6) of this Regulation, when the planing of squared stock of square cross section is being carried out, the bridge guard so provided shall be adjusted in a manner which complies with the requirements either of paragraph (2) or of paragraph (3) of this Regulation.

(6) When the planing of two adjoining surfaces of squared stock of square cross section is being carried out, one operation immediately following the other, the bridge guard so provided shall be adjusted so that neither the height of the underside of the guard above the feed table nor the distance between the end of the guard and the fence exceeds the width of the material by more than 10 millimetres.

(7) When the smoothing of squared stock of square cross section is being carried out, the bridge guard so provided shall be adjusted in a manner which complies with the requirements either of paragraph (2) or of paragraph (3) or of paragraph (6) of this Regulation.

Cutter block guards

28 (1) In addition to being provided with a bridge guard as required by Regulation 26, every planing machine for surfacing which is not mechanically fed shall be provided with a strong, effective and easily adjustable guard for that part of the cutter block which is on the side of the fence remote from the bridge guard.

(2) In the case of planing machines manufactured before the date of the coming into operation of this Regulation, the requirements of the foregoing paragraph of this Regulation shall not apply until twelve months after the said date.

Provision and use of push-blocks

29 When a wider surface of squared stock is being planed or smoothed and by reason of the shortness of the material the work cannot be done with the bridge guard adjusted as required by Regulation 27(2), a suitable push-block having suitable handholds which afford the operator a firm grip shall be provided and used.

Combined machines used for thicknessing

30 That part of the cutter block of a combined machine which is exposed in the table gap shall, when the said machine is used for thicknessing, be effectively guarded.

Protection against ejected material

31 (1) Every planing machine used for thicknessing shall be provided on the operator's side of the feed roller with sectional feed rollers, or other suitable devices which shall be of such a design and so constructed as to restrain so far as practicable any workpiece ejected by the machine.

(2) Paragraph (1) of this Regulation shall not apply to any machine manufactured before the date of coming into operation of this Regulation; provided that:

(*a*) not more than one work piece at a time shall be fed to any such machine, and (*b*) there shall be securely affixed to every such machine a notice specifying that only single pieces shall be fed.

PART VII

Vertical Spindle Moulding Machines

Construction, maintenance and mounting of cutters etc.

32 Every detachable cutter for any vertical spindle moulding machine shall be of the correct thickness for the cutter block or spindle on which it is to be mounted and shall be so mounted as to prevent it, so far as practicable, from becoming accidentally detached therefrom.

Provision of false fences

33 Where straight fences are being used for the purposes of the work being done as a vertical spindle moulding machine, the gap between the fences shall be reduced as far as practicable by a false fence or otherwise.

Provision of jigs or holders

34 Where by reason of the nature of the work being done at a vertical spindle moulding machine it is impracticable to provide in pursuance of Regulation 5 a guard enclosing the cutters of the said machine to such an extent that they are effectively guarded, but it is practicable to provide, in addition to the guard required to be provided by Regulation 5, a jig or holder of such a design and so constructed as to hold firmly the material being machined and having suitable handholds which afford the operator a firm grip, the machine shall not be used unless such a jig or holder is provided.

Design and construction of guards for protection against ejected parts

35 Every guard provided in pursuance of Regulation 5 for the cutters of any vertical spindle moulding machine shall be of such a design and so constructed as to contain, so far as reasonably practicable, any part of the cutters or their fixing appliances or any part thereof in the event of their ejection.

Provision and use of back stops

36 Where the work being done at a vertical spindle moulding machine is work in which the cutting of the material being machined commences otherwise than at the end of a surface of the said material and it is impracticable to provide a jig or holder in pursuance of Regulation 34, the trailing end of the said material shall if practicable be supported by a suitable back stop where this would prevent the said material being thrown back when the cutters first make contact with it.

Limitation on the use of vertical spindle moulding machines

37 No work shall be done on a vertical spindle moulding machine being work in which the cutting of the material being machined commences otherwise than at the end of a surface of the said material and during the progress of the cutting the material is moved in the same direction as the movement of the cutters, unless a jig or holder provided in pursuance of Regulation 34 is being used.

Provision of spikes or push-sticks

38 Where the nature of the work being performed at a vertical spindle moulding machine is such that the use of a suitable spike or push-stick would enable the work to be carried on without unnecessary risk, such a spike or push-stick shall be provided and kept available for use.

Machines driven by two speed motors

39 (1) Where the motor driving a vertical spindle moulding machine (other than a high-speed routing machine) is designed to operate at two working speeds the device controlling the speed of the motor shall be so arranged that the motor cannot run at the higher of those speeds, without first running at the lower of those speeds.

(2) In the case of machines manufactured before the coming into operation of this Regulation, the requirements of the foregoing paragraph of this Regulation shall not apply until twelve months after the said date.

PART VIII

Extraction Equipment and Maintenance

Cleaning of saw blades

40 The blade of a sawing machine shall not be cleaned by hand while the blade is in motion.

Extraction of chips and other particles

41 Effective exhaust appliances shall be provided and maintained at every planing machine used for thicknessing other than a combined machine for surfacing and thicknessing, every vertical spindle moulding machine, every multi-cutter moulding machine, every tenoning machine and every automatic lathe, for collecting from a position as close to the cutters as practicable and to the extent that is practicable, the chips and other particles of material removed by the action of the cutters and for discharging them into a suitable receptacle or place:

Provided that this Regulation shall not apply to any high-speed routing machine which incorporates means for blowing away from the cutters the chips or particles as they are removed or to either of the following which is not used for more than six hours in any week, that is to say, any vertical spindle moulding machine and any tenoning machine.

Maintenance and fixing

42 (1) Every woodworking machine and every part thereof, including cutters and cutter blocks, shall be of good construction, sound material and properly maintained.

(2) Every woodworking machine, other than a machine which is held in the hand, shall be securely fixed to a foundation, floor, or to a substantial part of the structure of the premises, save that where this is impracticable, other arrangements shall be made to ensure its stability.

PART IX

Lighting

43 In addition to the requirements of subsections (1) and (4) of section 5 of the principal Act and the Factories (Standards of Lighting) Regulations 1941 (a), the following provisions shall have effect in respect of any work done with any woodworking machine:

(a) the lighting, whether natural or artificial, for every woodworking machine shall be sufficient and suitable for the purpose for which the machine is used;

(b) the means of artificial lighting for every woodworking machine shall be so placed or shaded as to prevent glare and so that direct rays of light do not impinge on the eyes of the operator while he is operating such machine.

PART X

Noise

44 Where any factory, or any part thereof, is mainly used for work carried out on woodworking machines, the following provisions shall apply to that factory or part, as the case may be:

(a) where on any day any person employed is likely to be exposed continuously for 8 hours to a sound level of 90dB(A) or is likely to be subject to an equivalent or greater exposure to sound –

   (i) such measures as are reasonably practicable shall be taken to reduce noise to the greatest extent which is reasonably practicable; and

   (ii) suitable ear protectors shall be provided and made readily available for the use of every such person;

(b) all ear protectors provided in pursuance of the foregoing paragraph shall be maintained, and shall be used by the person for whom they are provided in any of the circumstances specified in paragraph (a) of this Regulation;

(c) for the purposes of paragraph (a) of this Regulation, the level of exposure which is equivalent to or greater than continuous exposure for 8 hours to a sound level of 90dB(A) shall be determined by an approved method.

Signed by order of the Secretary of State.

HAROLD WALKER,
Joint Parliamentary Under Secretary of State,
23rd May 1974   *Department of Employment.*

Schedule 1

Regulation 2(2)

Machines which are woodworking machines for the purposes of these Regulations
1. Any sawing machine designed to be fitted with one or more circular blades.
2. Grooving machines.
3. Any sawing machine designed to be fitted with a blade in the form of a continuous band or strip.
4. Chain sawing machines.
5. Mortising machines.
6. Planing machines.
7. Vertical spindle moulding machines (including high-speed routing machines).
8. Multi-cutter moulding machines having two or more cutter spindles.
9. Tenoning machines.
10. Trenching machines.
11. Automatic and semi-automatic lathes.
12. Boring machines.

Schedule 2

Regulation 1(2)

Column 1 Regulations revoked	Column 2 References	Column 3 Extent of Revocation
1. The Woodworking Machinery Regulations 1922.	S.R. & O. 1922/1196 (Rev. VII, p.458: 1922, p.273).	The whole Regulations.
2. The Woodworking Machinery (Amendment) Regulations 1927.	S.R. & O. 1927/207 (Rev. VII, p.462: 1927, p.440).	The whole Regulations.
3. The Woodworking (Amendment of Scope) Special Regulations 1945.	S.R. & O. 1945/1227 (Rev VII, p.462: 1945 I, p.380).	The whole Regulations.
4. The Railway Running Sheds (No. 2) Regulations 1961.	S.I. 1961/1768 (1961 III, p.3410).	In the Schedule, the items numbered 2, 5 and 9.

Explanatory Note

(This Note is not part of the Regulations)

These Regulations impose requirements as to guards and certain other safety devices for woodworking machines used in factories and certain other places to which the Factories Act 1961 applies.

The Regulations also impose requirements as to working space, condition of floors, noise, lighting and temperature in those factories and places and as to the training of persons operating woodworking machines.

The Regulations prohibit the sale or letting on hire for use in factories and other places to which the Regulations apply of woodworking machines which do not comply with specified provisions of the Regulations as to guards and other safety devices.

As respects guards and other safeguards for woodworking machines, the provisions of the Regulations are in substitution for the provisions of section 14(1) of the Factories Act 1961 and as respects the temperature of rooms, they are in substitution for the similar provisions of section 3(1) of the said Act.

Regulation 67(2) of the Shipbuilding and Ship-repairing Regulations 1960 and Regulation 42 of the Construction (General Provisions) Regulations 1961 (which require the secure fencing of dangerous parts of machinery) are amended so that they no longer apply to the parts of woodworking machines required by these Regulations to be guarded or to have other safeguards.

The Regulations supersede the Woodworking Machinery Special Regulations 1922 to 1945 which are revoked.

Self-assessment questions

1 Thrust wheels are fitted to which one of the
   following machines?
   (a) dimension saw
   (b) hand woodworking lathe
   (c) narrow band saw
   (d) chain mortiser

2 The cutter block guard on a surface planer is
   known as the
   (a) shaw guard
   (b) top guard
   (c) crown guard
   (d) bridge guard

3 The machine normally used to 'face and edge'
   a length of timber is a
   (a) surface planer
   (b) panel planer
   (c) spindle moulder
   (d) dimension saw

4 One way of obtaining a smooth finish when
   machine planing a length of joinery timber is
   to
   (a) use a slow feed-speed
   (b) increase the pressure on the timber
   (c) use a fast feed-speed
   (d) decrease the pressure on the timber

5 When stripping old varnish off internal panel
   doors the best machine or power tool to use
   would be
   (a) a surface planer
   (b) a belt sander
   (c) a combination machine
   (d) an orbital sander

6 The first operation that must be carried out,
   before setting up and starting to use any
   machine, is to
   (a) clean up around the machine
   (b) isolate the power supply

   (c) sharpen the cutters
   (d) set up the guards

7 The riving knife fitted to circular sawing
   machines must have a maximum clearance
   gap between itself and the blade of
   (a) 6 mm
   (b) 10 mm
   (c) 12 mm
   (d) 20 mm

8 The correct way to wire up a 13 amp, three-
   pin plug is

	live pin	neutral pin	earth pin
(a)	brown	blue	yellow/green
(b)	yellow/green	brown	blue
(c)	blue	brown	yellow/green
(d)	brown	yellow/green	blue

Figure 92   *Self-assessment question*

9 The circular saw blade shown in Figure 92 is
   for
   (a) cross-cutting
   (b) rip sawing
   (c) rip sawing hardwood
   (d) both rip sawing and cross-cutting

10 The safest voltage to use on site for operating
   portable power tools is
   (a) 220 volts
   (b) 440 volts
   (c) 110 volts
   (d) 55 volts

chapter 3

Materials

After reading this chapter you should be able to:

1 Describe, with the aid of sketches where appropriate, the growth, structure and characteristics of hard and softwoods.

2 Describe the various methods of timber conversion.

3 Describe two methods and the purpose of timber seasoning.

4 List and sketch the main timber defects.

5 Describe the main causes of timber decay and procedures to be followed for their prevention and eradication.

6 State the various types and methods of application of timber preservatives.

7 Describe the composition of a number of timber-based manufactured boards.

8 List and state the uses and characteristics of the main woodworking adhesives.

9 Recognize and select suitable ironmongery for a given purpose.

10 State the composition and properties of concrete.

Timber

The growth of a tree

Trees grow by adding a new layer of wood cells below the bark each growing season (usually each year). Figure 93 shows the process involved to produce these new cells. Water and minerals (raw sap) are absorbed from the soil by the roots and travel up through the sapwood to the leaves. There a process called photosynthesis occurs, using sunlight which is absorbed by the green substance in the leaves (chlorophyll). During this process carbon dioxide is absorbed and oxygen is given off, and as a result sugar is formed. The sugar is then added to the water and minerals. This enriched sap passes down the tree through the inner bark to the cambium layer. This layer consists of a ring of cells which divide to form the new layer of growth. Surplus foods are stored in cells which radiate from the centre of the tree, which are called medullary rays.

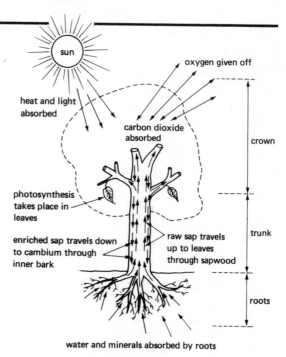

Figure 93 *The growth of a tree*

Figure 93 also shows the three main areas of a tree.

The *roots* as well as absorbing water and minerals from the soil, also act as a form of anchor for the tree.

The *trunk* is the main timber producing part of the tree.

The *crown* consists of the branches and the leaves.

Cross-section of a tree trunk (Figure 94)
Bark is the corky outer layer of the tree which protects it against external damage.

Bast, also known as the inner bark, carries the enriched sap down from the leaves to all the growing parts of the tree. The outer layers of the bast progressively die off and form new layers of bark. The old bark scales off as the tree increases in size.

The *cambium* is a thin layer of living cells under the bast. The cells divide to form new wood cells and new bast cells during the growing season.

Sapwood is the newly formed outer layers of growth which convey the rising unenriched sap up to the leaves. As the sapwood contains food-stuffs, it is considered to be prone to insect and fungi attack, unless it has been treated with a preservative.

Heartwood is the inner, more mature part of the tree which no longer conveys the sap. The heartwood's main function is to give strength to the tree. In many timbers it is often darker and harder than the sapwood.

Annual rings are also known as growth rings. In cool countries, including Britain, the growth takes place mainly in the spring and summer months and an annual growth ring is formed. In tropical countries the tree's growth can be almost continuous and sometimes it is virtually impossible to distinguish between each year's growth ring.

Pith is also known as the medulla. It is the first growth of the tree and often decays as the tree gets older.

Medullary rays are groups of food-storing cells which radiate from the pith or medulla of the tree.

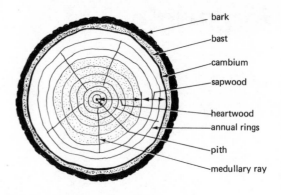

Figure 94   *Cross-section of a tree trunk*

Structure
All commercial timber is divided into two groups. These are:

Softwoods (coniferous)
Hardwoods (broadleaf)

This grouping has nothing to do with the hardness of the timber concerned, but is based solely on its structure.

Generally, a clear difference exists between softwood and hardwood trees.

General identifying characteristics of softwood trees (Figure 95)
1   A trunk which is very straight and cylindrical with an even taper.
2   A crown that is narrow and pointed.
3   Needle-like leaves.
4   A bark which is coarse and thick.
5   The seeds are borne in cones.
6   They are evergreen, i.e. they do not drop all their leaves at once in the autumn.

General identifying characteristics of hardwood trees (Figure 96)
1   An irregular, less cylindrical trunk, which very often has little taper.
2   A crown which is wide, rounded and contains large heavy branches.
3   They have broad leaves.
4   The bark varies widely. It can be very smooth and thin to very coarse and thick, and range from white to black in colour.

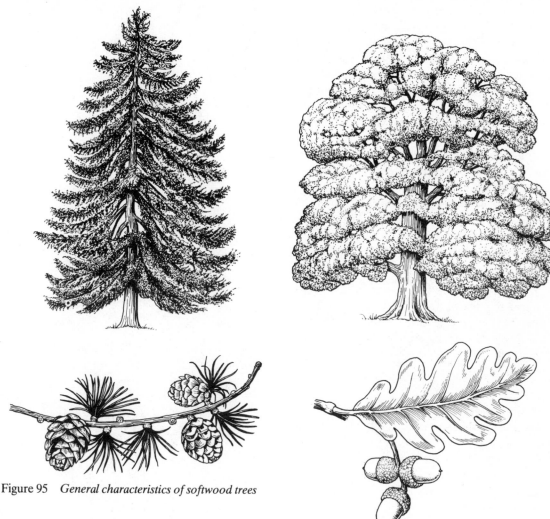

Figure 95   *General characteristics of softwood trees*

Figure 96   *General characteristics of hardwood trees*

5 They have covered seeds, e.g. berries, acorns and stoned fruits, etc.
6 They are mainly deciduous, e.g. they shed their leaves in winter.

Apart from these differences in general characteristics, there are more important differences between the cellular structure of the two types of trees.

Softwood structure
Softwood trees have a simple structure, with only two types of cell, tracheids and parenchyma. See Figure 97.

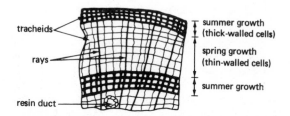

Figure 97   *Magnified softwood section*

Tracheids are box-like cells which form the main structural tissue of the wood and, as well as giving the tree its mechanical strength, they also conduct the rising sap. The sap passes from one tracheid to another through thin areas of the cell's wall known as pits. Tracheids are formed throughout the tree's growing season, but the rapid spring growth produces a wide band of thin-walled cells (called early wood). These cells conduct sap but provide little strength. It is the summer growth of thick-walled cells (called late wood) which provide most of the trees mechanical strength.

Parenchyma cells are food-storing cells which radiate from the centre of the tree. These are also known as ray parenchyma or medullary rays.

Resin ducts or pockets are also found in softwood but perform no useful function.

Note: Slow grown softwoods are considered to be stronger than fast grown softwoods. This is because the slow grown timber contains more thick-walled, strength-giving tracheids than the fast grown. This is illustrated in Figure 98.

Hardwood structure

Hardwood trees have a more complex structure consisting of three types of cell, fibres, parenchyma and vessels or pores.

Fibres are the main structural tissue of the wood, giving it its mechanical strength.

Parenchyma cells perform the same function as they do in softwood, i.e. store food.

Vessels or *pores* are sap-conducting cells. These cells are circular or oval in section and can occur in the annual ring in one of two ways:

They can be of a uniform size and be spread or diffused fairly evenly throughout the year's growth. Trees of this type are known as diffuse porous hardwoods. Figure 99.

They can form a definite ring of large cells in the early spring growth, with smaller cells spread throughout the growing season. These are known as ring porous hardwoods. Figure 100.

Note: Fast grown, ring porous hardwoods are considered to be stronger than slow grown, ring porous hardwoods. This is because there is less

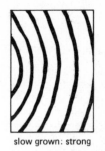

slow grown: strong   fast grown: weak

Figure 98   *Fast and slow grown softwood*

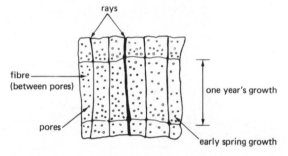

rays

fibre (between pores)

one year's growth

pores

early spring growth

Figure 99   *Magnified diffused porous hardwood section*

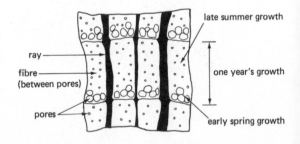

late summer growth

ray

fibre (between pores)

one year's growth

pores

early spring growth

Figure 100   *Magnified ring porous hardwood section*

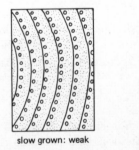
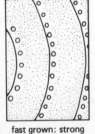

slow grown: weak   fast grown: strong

Figure 101   *Fast and slow grown hardwood*

room for the strength-giving fibres between the pores in the slow grown timber. This is illustrated in Figure 101.

Conversion of timber

The conversion of timber is the sawing up or breaking down of the tree trunk into various-sized pieces of timber for a specific purpose.

Theoretically a tree trunk can be sawn to the required size in one of two ways:

By sawing in a tangential direction. See Figure 102.

By sawing in a radial direction. See Figure 102.

The terms radial and tangential refer to the cut surfaces of the timber in relation to the growth rings of the tree. Both methods have their own advantages and disadvantages.

In practice very little timber is cut either truly tangentially or radially because there would be too much wastage in both timber and manpower.

To be classified as either a tangential or a radial cut, the timber must conform to the following standards:

Tangential. Timber converted so that the annual rings meet the wider surface of the timber over at least half its width, at an angle of less than 45 degrees. See Figure 103.

Radial. Timber converted so that the annual rings meet the wider surface of the timber throughout its width at an angle of 45 degrees or more. See Figure 104.

There are four main methods of conversion to produce timber to these standards.

Through and through
Tangential
Quarter
Boxed heart

Through and through (Figure 105)
This method is also known as slash or slab sawing. It is the simplest and cheapest way to convert timber, with very little wastage.

Note: Approximately two-thirds of the boards will be tangential and one-third (the middle boards) will be radial.

The majority of boards produced in this way are prone to a large amount of shrinkage and distortion.

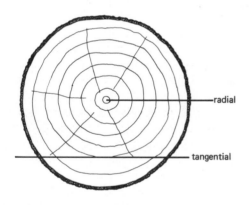

Figure 102   *Timber conversion*

Figure 103   *Tangential cut. Annual rings at less than 45°*

Figure 104   *Radial cut. Annual rings at 45° or more*

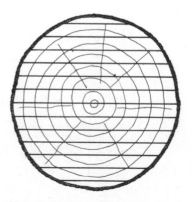

Figure 105   *Through and through*

Tangential (Figure 106)

This method is used when converting timber for floor joists and beams, since it produces the strongest timber. It is also used for decorative purposes on timbers which have distinctive annual rings, e.g. pitch pine and Douglas fir, because it produces 'flame figuring' or 'fiery grain'.

Quarter (Figure 107)

This is the most expensive method of conversion, although it produces the best quality timber which is ideal for joinery purposes. This is because the boards have very little tendency to shrink or distort.

In timber where the medullary rays are prominent, the boards will have a figured finish, e.g. figured or silver-grained oak.

Boxed heart (Figure 108)

This is a type of radial sawing and is done when the heart of a tree is rotten or badly shaken. It is also known as floor board sawing as the boards produced are ideal for this purpose because they wear well and do not distort. The waste pieces of timber are of an inferior quality but are often used for fencing, etc.

Types of machine

There are three main types of machine used to convert round tree trunks into square section timber.

The circular saw mill

This is also known as a rack saw bench. It consists of a circular saw blade of up to 2.1 m in diameter and a travelling table on to which the tree trunk is fastened.

The log band mill

This can be of either the horizontal or vertical type. Both types consist of a continuous band saw blade, up to 250 mm in width, mounted on two large-diameter pulleys and a travelling carriage on to which the tree trunk is fastened. The carriage runs on a track and feeds the tree trunk through the saw.

The log frame saw

This consists of a number of vertically mounted saw blades which move up and down in a frame. The tree trunk is fed through the saw by large feed rollers.

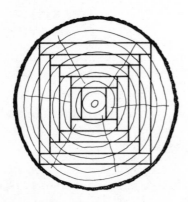

Figure 106   *Tangential*

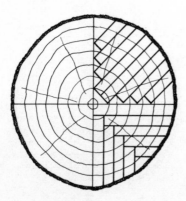

Figure 107   *Quarter cut*

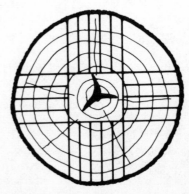

Figure 108   *Boxed heart cut*

Seasoning

The term *seasoning* refers to the controlled drying by natural or artificial means of converted timber. There are many reasons why seasoning is necessary, the main ones being:

To ensure the moisture content of the timber is below the dry rot safety line of 20 per cent.

To ensure that any shrinkage takes place before the timber is used.

Dry timber is easier to work with than wet timber.

Using seasoned timber, the finished article will be more reliable and less likely to split or distort.

In general, dry timber is stronger and stiffer than wet timber.

Wet timber will not readily accept glue, paint or polish.

Moisture

Moisture occurs in the timber in two forms:

As free water in the cell cavities.
As bound water in the cell walls.

When all of the free water in the cell cavities has been removed, the fibre saturation point is reached. At this point the timber normally has a moisture content of between 25 and 30 per cent. It is only when the moisture content of the timber is reduced below the fibre saturation point that shrinkage occurs. The amount of shrinkage is not the same in all directions. The majority of shrinkage takes place tangentially, i.e. in the direction of the annual rings. Radial shrinkage is approximately half that of tangential shrinkage, while shrinkage in length is virtually non-existent and can be disregarded. See Figure 109.

The timber should be dried out to a moisture content which is approximately equal to the surrounding atmosphere in which it will be used. This moisture content is known as the equilibrium moisture content and, providing the moisture content and temperature of the air remains constant, the timber will remain stable and not shrink or expand. But in most situations the moisture content of the atmosphere will vary to some extent and sometimes this variation can be quite considerable.

Timber fixed in a moist atmosphere will absorb moisture and expand. If it was then fixed in a dry atmosphere the bound moisture in the cells of the timber would dry out and the timber would start to shrink. This is exactly what happens during seasonal changes in the weather. Therefore all timber is subject to a certain amount of moisture movement and this must be allowed for in all construction and joinery work.

The moisture content of timber is expressed as a percentage. This refers to the weight of the water in the timber compared to the dry weight of the timber.

In order to determine the average moisture content of a stack of timber, select a board from the centre of the stack, cut the end 300 mm off and discard it as this will normally be dryer than sections nearer the centre. Cut off a further 25 mm sample and immediately weigh it. This is the wet weight of the sample. Place this sample in a small drying oven and remove it periodically to check its weight. When no further loss of weight is recorded, assume this to be the dry weight of the sample.

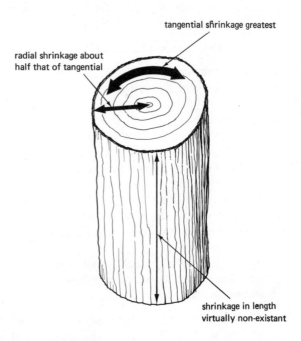

Figure 109 *Shrinkage*

The moisture content of a piece of timber can now be found by using the following formula:

moisture content (per cent) =

$$\frac{\text{wet weight} - \text{dry weight}}{\text{dry weight}} \times 100$$

Example
Wet weight of sample 50 g
Dry weight of sample 40 g

$$\text{moisture content} = \frac{50 - 40}{40} \times 100 = 25 \text{ per cent}$$

Use	Moisture content (per cent)
Carcassing timber	18 – 20
External joinery	16 – 18
Internal timber with a partial, intermittent heating system	14 – 16
Internal timber with a continuous heating system	10 – 12
Internal timber placed directly over or near sources of heat	7 – 10

Table 1

An alternative way of finding the moisture content of timber is to use an electric moisture meter. Although not as accurate, it has the advantage of giving an on-the-spot reading and it can even be used for determining the moisture content of timber already fixed in position. The moisture meter measures the electrical resistance between the two points of a twin electrode which is pushed into the surface of the timber. Its moisture content can then easily be read off a calibrated dial.

The ideal moisture content for timber used in various locations is listed in Table 1.

Timber may be seasoned in one of two ways:

By natural means (air seasoning)
By artificial means (kiln seasoning)

Air seasoning
In this method the timber is stacked in open sided, covered sheds which protect the timber from rain whilst still allowing a free circulation of air.

In Britain a moisture content of between 18 per cent and 20 per cent can be achieved in a period of two to twelve months, depending on the size and type of timber.

Figure 110 shows an ideal timber stack for the air seasoning of softwoods. The following points should be noted:

1 Brick piers and timber joists keep the bottom of the stack well clear of the ground and ensure good air circulation underneath.

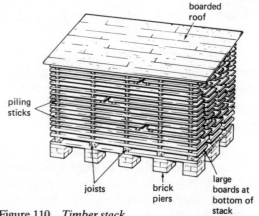

Figure 110   *Timber stack*

2 The boards are laid horizontally, largest at the bottom, smallest at the top, one piece above the other. This reduces the risk of the timber distorting as it dries out.

3 The boards on each layer are spaced approximately 25 mm apart.

4 Piling sticks or stickers are introduced between each layer of timber at approximately 600 mm distances, to support the boards and allow a free air circulation around them.
   Note: The piling sticks should be the same type of timber as that being seasoned otherwise staining may occur.

5 The ends of the boards should be painted or covered with strips of timber to prevent them from drying out too quickly and splitting.

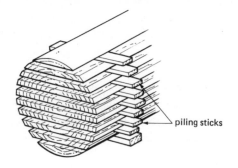

Figure 111   *Hardwood stacked for seasoning*

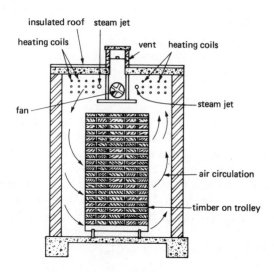

Figure 112   *Compartment kiln*

Hardwood can be seasoned in the same air-seasoning sheds but the boards should be stacked in the same order as they were cut from the log, as shown in Figure 111.

Kiln seasoning

Most timber for internal use is kiln seasoned, as this method, if carried out correctly, is able to safely reduce the moisture content of the timber to any required level, without any danger of degrading (causing defects). Although timber can be completely kiln seasoned, sometimes when a saw mill has a low kiln capacity, the timber is air seasoned before being placed in the kiln for final seasoning. The length of time the timber needs to stay in the kiln normally varies between two days and six weeks according to the type and size of timber being seasoned.

There are two main types of kiln in general use:

The compartment kiln
The progressive kiln

The *compartment kiln* is normally a brick or concrete building in which the timber is stacked. The timber will remain stationary during the drying process, while the conditions of the air are adjusted to the correct levels as the drying progresses.

Note: The timber should be stacked in the same way as that used for air seasoning.

Figure 112 shows a section through a compartment kiln in which the drying of the timber depends on three factors:

Air circulation, which is supplied by fans.

Heat, which is normally supplied by heating coils through which steam flows.

Humidity (moisture content of the air). Steam sprays are used for raising the humidity. They are installed along the whole length of the compartment.

The *progressive kiln* can be thought of as a tunnel, full of open trucks containing timber which are progressively moved forward from the loading end to the discharge end. The drying conditions in the kiln become progressively more severe so that loads at different distances from the loading end are at different stages of drying.

Progressive kilns are mainly used in situations where there is a need for a continuous supply of timber, which is of the same species and dimensions.

Drying schedules are available for the kiln drying of different types of timbers. These set out the drying conditions required for a given size and type of timber. Although all types of timber require different conditions for varying lengths of time, the drying process in general involves three stages, these being:

1   Wet timber inserted; controls set to high steam, low heat.

2 Timber drying; controls set to reduce steam, increase heat.
3 Timber almost dry; controls set to low steam, high heat. The seasoned timber can then be removed from the kiln.

Second seasoning

This is rarely carried out nowadays, but refers to a further drying of high-class joinery work after it has been machined and loosely framed up, but not glued or wedged. The framed joinery is stacked in a store which has a similar moisture content to the building where it will be finally fixed. Should any defects occur during this second seasoning, which can last up to three months, the defective component can easily be replaced.

Water seasoning

This is not seasoning as we understand it at all. It refers to timber logs which are kept under water before conversion in order to protect them from timber decay. This process is also sometimes used to wash out the sap of some hardwoods, which is particularly susceptible to attack by the *Lyctus* beetle.

Conditioning

This is a form of reverse seasoning. It refers to the practice of brushing up to one litre of water on the back of hardboard twenty-four to forty-eight hours before fixing. This is so that the board will tighten on its fixings as it dries out and shrinks. If this were not done, expansion could take place which would result in the board bowing or buckling.

Storage of seasoned timber

As the seasoning of timber is a reversible process, great care must be taken in the storage of seasoned timber. Carcassing timber and external joinery will normally be delivered to a site at an early stage. This should be stacked clear of the ground using piling sticks between each layer or item and covered with waterproof tarpaulins. Internal joinery items should not be delivered to a site until a suitable store is available to receive them. Before low moisture timber is delivered or instal-led, the building should be fully glazed and its heating system in operation, or if this is not possible a temporary heating system should be used to dry out the building and maintain a low humidity.

Defects in timber

Timber is subject to many defects which should, as far as possible, be cut out during its conversion. These defects can be divided into two groups:

Seasoning defects
Natural defects

Seasoning defects

Bowing (Figure 113). This is a curvature along the face of a board, and often occurs where insufficient piling sticks are used during seasoning.

Springing (Figure 114). This is a curvature along the edge of the board where the face remains flat. It is often caused through bad conversion or curved grain.

Winding (Figure 115). This is a twisting of the board and often occurs in timber which is not converted parallel to the pith of the tree.

Cupping (Figure 116). This is a curvature across the width of the board and is due to the fact that timber shrinks more tangentially than it does radially.

Shaking (Figure 117). These are splits which develop along the grain of a piece of timber, particularly at its ends, and is the result of the surface or ends of the timber drying out too fast during seasoning.

Collapse (Figure 118). This is also known as wash boarding and is caused by the cells collapsing through being kiln dried too rapidly.

Case hardening (Figure 119). This is also the result of too rapid kiln drying. In this case the outside of the board is dry but moisture is trapped in the centre cells of the timber. This defect is not apparent until the board is re-sawn when it will tend to twist.

Natural defects in timber

Heart shakes (Figure 120). These are splits along the heart of a tree and are probably due to over-maturity.

Figure 113   *Bowing*

Figure 114   *Springing*

Figure 115   *Winding*

Figure 116   *Cupping*

Figure 117   *Shaking*

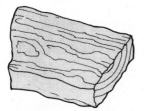

Figure 118   *Collapse*

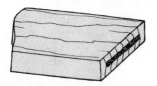

Figure 119   *Case hardening*

Figure 120   *Heart shakes*

Figure 121   *Star shakes*

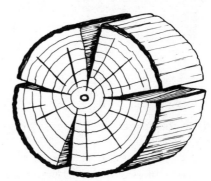

Figure 122   *Radial shakes*

Star shakes (Figure 121). These are a number of heart shakes which form an approximate star.

Radial shakes (Figure 122). These are splits along the outside of the log, which are caused by the rapid drying of the outside of the log before it is converted.

Cup shakes (Figure 123). This is a separation between the annual rings and is normally the result of a lack of nutriment. It is also said to be

Figure 123   *Cup shakes*

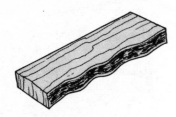

Figure 124   *Waney edge*

Figure 125   *Knots*

caused by the rising sap freezing during early spring cold spells.

Waney edge (Figure 124). This is where the bark is left on the edge of converted timber and is the result of too economical a conversion.

Knots (Figure 125). These are the end sections of branches where they grow out of the trunk. Knots can be considered as being either sound, i.e. knots which are firm in their socket and show no signs of decay, or dead, i.e. knots which have become loose in their sockets or show signs of decay.

All knots can be a serious defect in timber but this is especially true of dead knots. The presence of knots on the surface of a piece of timber often causes difficulties when finishing because of the

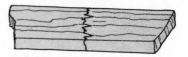

Figure 126   *Upsets*

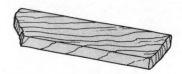

Figure 127   *Sloping grain*

distorted grain which the knots cause. Although mainly considered to be a defect, knots are sometimes used to provide a decorative feature, e.g. knotty pine cladding.

Upsets (Figure 126). This defect is also known as thunder shake and is a fracture of the timber fibres across the grain. Upsets can be caused by the tree being struck by lightning some time during its growth, but they are mainly caused by the severe jarring the tree receives when being felled. This is a serious defect, which is most common in mahogany and is not apparent until the timber has been planed.

Sloping grain (Figure 127). This is where the grain does not run parallel to the edge of the board and is often caused by bad conversion. When the sloping grain is pronounced, the defect is called short graining. This seriously affects the strength of the timber and it should not be used for structural work.

Sap stain. This is also known as blue sap stain or blueing and often occurs in felled logs while still in the forest. It can also occur in damp timber that has been improperly stacked close together without piling sticks or with insufficient air circulation. The stain is the result of a harmless fungus feeding on the contents of the sapwood cells. No structural damage is caused by this fungus and it is only normally considered as a defect in timber that is to have a polished or clear varnish finish.

Building timbers
Table 2 gives details of a number of building timbers which are in common use.

Building timbers in common use

Timber	Source	Colour	Main uses
European Redwood (softwood)	Europe	Pale red, brown heartwood. Light yellow, brown sapwood	All general carpentry and joinery work (roofs, floors, doors and windows)
Douglas Fir (softwood)	Canada and USA	Pale brown	All general carpentry and joinery work (normally of a higher class than European Redwood), plywood
Western Red Cedar (softwood)	Canada and USA	Pink to red-brown	Interior and exterior joinery, cladding, panelling and roof coverings (shingles)
Parana Pine (softwood)	South America	Light to dark brown with red streaks	Interior joinery and fittings
Oak (hardwood)	Europe, America and Japan	Light brown with silver streaks	Panelling, external joinery, church fittings, floor and roof timbers
Teak (hardwood)	Burma and Thailand	Mid-brown, often with greenish tints	High-class joinery, ship joinery, laboratory fittings
Beech (hardwood)	Europe and Japan	Light brown with golden flecks	Furniture, plywood and floor coverings
Mahogany (hardwood)	West Africa and South America	Pink to red-brown	Panelling, cabinet work, flooring and joinery

Table 2

Supply of timber

Softwoods can usually be obtained in all the stock sizes and lengths in Figure 128. Hardwood on the other hand is normally only available in a very limited range of sizes which vary from merchant to merchant. There are four main units in which timber can be purchased.

1 By the cubic metre (m³). This is the unit normally used by the majority of large building and joinery firms.
2 By the square metre (m²). This is traditionally the unit used to purchase floorboarding and cladding.
3 By width, thickness and length. This method is used to purchase small amounts of timber.
4 By length. This method is used to purchase pre-machined mouldings, skirtings, architraves, cover moulds, sash stock, etc.

The size of timber is often referred to in the timber, woodworking and building trades by the terms listed in Table 3.

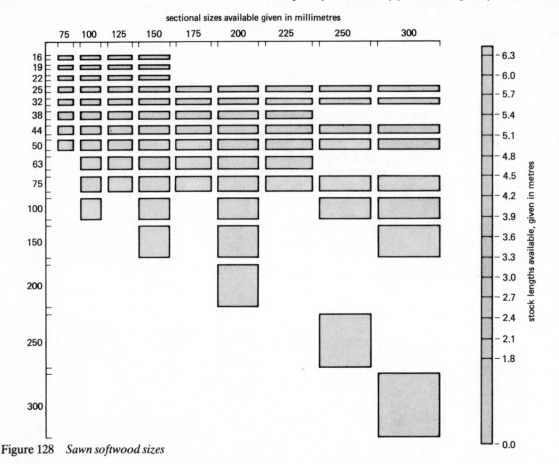

Figure 128   *Sawn softwood sizes*

Term	Definition
Log	A trimmed tree trunk
Butt	A short log
Baulk	A squared log
Die-squared	The same as a baulk
Plank	Sawn softwood, between 50 mm and 100 mm in thickness and over 275 mm in width
Deal	Sawn softwood, between 50 mm and 100 mm in thickness and between 225 mm and 275 mm in width. *Note:* This term is normally only used for 50 mm × 225 mm timbers
Batten	Sawn softwood, between 50 mm and 100 mm in thickness and between 100 mm and 200 mm in width *Note:* This term is also used for tile battens, etc., of up to approximately 25 × 50 mm in section
Board	Sawn softwood, under 50 mm in thickness and more than 100 mm in width
Scantling	Sawn softwood, between 50 mm and 100 mm in thickness and between 50 mm and 112 mm in width
Dimension stock	Timber which has been converted to standard sizes

Table 3

Decay of timber

The decay of building timber is caused mainly by one or both of the following:

An attack by wood-destroying fungi.
An attack by wood-boring insects. This is covered in *Carpentry and Joinery for Building Craft Students 2*.

Wood-destroying fungi

Dry rot

The most common type of wood-destroying fungus is *Merulius lacrymans*. Its common name is dry rot or weeping fungus. As well as being the most common, it is also more serious and more difficult to eradicate than any other fungus.

Dry rot attacks the cellulose found mainly in sapwood and causes the affected timber to:

Loose strength and weight.
Develop cracks, both with and across the grain.
Become so dry and powdery that it can be easily
    crumbled in the hand.

The two initial factors for an attack of dry rot in timber are:

1 Damp timber (i.e. timber with a moisture content above 20 per cent)
    Note: 20 per cent is known as the dry rot safety line.
2 Bad or non-existent ventilation (e.g. no circulation of air)

Given these two conditions and a temperature above freezing, an attack by dry rot is practically certain.

Stages of attack

An attack of dry rot occurs in three stages.

Stage 1. The microscopic spores (seeds) of the fungus are blown about in the wind and are already present in most timbers. Given the right conditions, these spores will germinate and send out hyphae (fine hair-like rootlets) which bore into the timber surface. See Figure 129.

Stage 2. The hyphae branch out and spread through and over the surface of the timber, forming a mat of cotton-wool-like threads called a mycelium. It is at this stage that the hyphae can

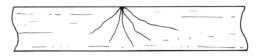

Figure 129   *Dry rot attack, stage 1: spores land on damp timber and send out hyphae*

Figure 130   *Dry rot attack, stage 2: hyphae branch out and form mycelium and a fruiting body starts to grow*

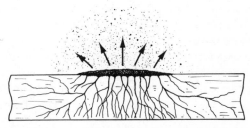

Figure 131   *Dry rot attack, stage 3: fruiting body ripens and starts to eject millions of spores into the air*

start to penetrate plaster and brickwork in search of new timber to attack. The hyphae are also able to conduct water and this enables them to adjust the water content of the new timber to the required level for their continued growth. Once the mycelium becomes sufficiently prolific a fruiting body will start to form. See Figure 130.

Stage 3. The fruiting body, which is like a large fleshy pancake, with a white border and an orange-brown centre, starts to ripen. When fully ripe, the fruiting body starts to discharge into the air millions of rust-red spores which begin the process elsewhere. See Figure 131.

Prevention

As the two main factors for the growth of dry rot are damp timber and bad ventilation, by paying attention to the following points an attack of dry rot can be prevented:

Always keep all timber dry (even before fixing into the building).

Always ensure good ventilation.

> *Note:* All constructional timbers should be placed so as to allow a free circulation of air around them.

Always use well seasoned timber.

Always use preservative-treated timbers in unfavourable or vulnerable positions.

Recognition

Very often in the early stages there is little evidence of a dry rot attack on the surface of the timber. It is not until panelling, skirting boards or floor boards, etc., are removed that the full effect of an attack is realized.

When dry rot is suspected a simple test is to probe the surface of the timber with a small penknife blade. If there is little resistance when the blade is inserted, there is a good possibility that dry rot is present. In addition to the other results of dry rot previously mentioned, the presence of a damp musty smell can also be taken as an indication of the presence of some form of fungal attack.

Eradication

By following the stages in the order given, an attack of dry rot can be successfully eradicated.

Stage 1. Increase the ventilation and cure the cause of the dampness which may be one or a combination of any of the following:

Cracked or missing roof tiles.

Defective flashings to parapet walls and chimneys, etc.

Defective drains and gulleys.

Defective, bridged or non-existent damp proof course.

Defective plumbing, including leaking gutters, down pipes, radiators, sinks, basins or w.c., etc.

Blocked, or an insufficient number of, air bricks.

Stage 2. Remove all traces of the rot. This involves cutting away all the infected timber and at least 600 mm of apparently sound wood beyond the last signs of attack, since this may also have been penetrated by the hyphae.

Stage 3. Burn immediately, on the site, all the infected timber, and all materials which are likely to contain traces of the fungus, including dust, dirt, old shavings, sawdust and insulating material, etc.

Stage 4. Strip the plaster from the walls at least 600 mm beyond the last signs of hyphae growth.

Stage 5. Clean off all brickwork with a wire brush and sterilize the walls by playing a blow lamp flame over them until the bricks are too hot to touch. While still warm, brush or spray the walls with a dry rot fungicide. Apply a second coat when the first is dry.

Stage 6. Treat all existing sound timber with three coats of a dry rot preservative. This can be applied by either a brush or spray.

Stage 7. Replace all timber which has been taken out with properly seasoned timber, which has also been treated with three coats of dry rot preservative, or timber which has been pressure impregnated with a preservative.

Note: All fresh surfaces which have been exposed by cutting or drilling, must also be treated with a preservative.

Wet rot

This is another common type of wood-destroying fungus which is also known as cellar rot. Its name is *Coniophora cerebella*.

Wet rot is mainly found in wet rather than damp conditions such as:

Cellars

Neglected external joinery

Ends of rafters

Under leaking sinks or baths

Under impervious (waterproof) floor coverings

Recognition

The timber becomes considerably darker in colour and has longitudinal cracks (along the grain). Very often the timber decays internally with a fairly thin skin of apparently sound timber remaining on the surface. The hyphae of wet rot, when apparent, are yellowish but quickly turn to dark brown or black. Fruiting bodies, which are rarely found, are thin, irregular in shape and olive green in colour. The spores are also olive green.

Eradication

Wet rot does not normally involve such drastic treatment as dry rot as wet rot does not spread to adjoining dry timber.

All that is normally required to eradicate an attack of wet rot is to cure the source of wetness. Where the decay has become extensive, or where structural timber is affected some replacement will be necessary.

Preservation of timber

All timbers, especially their sapwood, contain food on which fungi and insects live. The idea behind timber preservation is to poison the food supply by applying a toxic liquid to the timber.

The ideal requirements of a timber preservative are as follows:

It must be toxic to the fungi and insects, but safe to animals and humans.
It should be permanent and not liable to be bleached out by sunshine or leached out by rain.
It should be economical and easy to obtain.
It should not corrode or affect metal in any way.
It should be easy to handle and apply.
It should, as far as possible, be odourless.
It should not affect the subsequent finishing of the timber, e.g. painting or polishing.
It should be non-inflammable.

Note: Although these are the ideal requirements of a preservative bear in mind that most preservatives will not embody all of these points. Care should be taken therefore to select the best type of preservative for the work in hand.

There are three main types of timber preservative available, these being:

Tar oils
Water-soluble preservatives
Organic solvent preservatives

Tar oils

These are derived from coal and are dark brown or black in colour. They are fairly permanent, cheap, effective and easy to apply. However, they should not be used internally, as they are inflammable and possess a strong lingering odour. They should never be used near food stuffs as odour will contaminate them. The timber once treated will not accept any further finish e.g. it cannot be painted. Its main uses are for the treatment of external timber such as fences, sheds, telegraph poles, etc.

Water-soluble preservatives

These are toxic chemicals which are mixed with water. They are suitable for use in both internal and external situations. The wood can be painted subsequently and they are odourless and non-inflammable.

Note: As the toxic chemicals are water-soluble some of the types available are prone to leaching out when in wet or damp conditions.

Organic solvent preservatives

These consist of toxic chemicals which are mixed with a spirit that evaporates after the preservative has been applied. This is an advantage because the moisture content of the timber is not increased. The use and characteristics of these types of preservative are similar to those of water-soluble preservatives, but with certain exceptions. Some of the solvents used are inflammable so care must be taken when applying or storing them. Some types also have a strong odour. In general organic solvent preservatives are the most expensive type to use but are normally considered to be superior because of their excellent preservation properties.

Methods of application

To a large extent it is the method of application rather than the preservative that governs the degree of protection obtained. This is because each method of application gives a different depth of preservative penetration. The greater the depth of penetration the higher the degree of protection. Preservatives can be applied using a number of methods but all of these can be classed in two groups:

Non-pressure treatment, e.g. brushing, spraying, dipping and steeping.
Pressure treatment, e.g. empty-cell process and full-cell process.

Non-pressure treatment

Brushing. In this method the preservative is brushed on. It can be used for all types but the effect is very limited as only a surface coating is achieved (very little penetration of the preservative into the timber).

Spraying. The preservative is sprayed on, but the effect is similar to brushing, i.e. little penetration is achieved.

Dipping. In this method the timber is immersed in a container full of preservative. After a certain length of time the timber is taken out and allowed to drain. The depth of penetration depends upon the length of time that the timber is immersed. Although better than brushing or spraying, penetration may still be very limited.

Steeping. This is known as the hot and cold method. The timber is immersed in large tanks containing the preservative. The preservative is then heated for about two hours and then the heat is removed and the preservative is allowed to cool. As the preservative is heated, the air in the cells of the timber expands and escapes as bubbles to the surface. On cooling the preservative is sucked into the spaces left by the air. Fairly good penetration can be achieved, making this by far the best non-pressure method.

Pressure treatment

This is the most effective form of timber preservation as full penetration of the cells is achieved.

Empty-cell process. The timber is placed in a sealed cylinder. The air in the cylinder is then subjected to pressure which causes the air in the timber cells to compress. At this stage preservative is run into the cylinder and the pressure increased further. This forces the preservative into the timber. The pressure is maintained at this high level until the required amount of penetration is achieved. The pressure is then released and the surplus preservative is pumped back into a storage container. As the air pressure is reduced, the compressed air in the cells expands and forces out most of the preservative, leaving only the cell walls coated.

Full-cell process. The timber is placed into the sealed cylinder as before but this time, instead of compressing the air, it is drawn out. This creates a vacuum in the cylinder, as well as a partial one in the cells of the timber. At this stage the preservative is introduced into the cylinder. When the cylinder is full, the vacuum is released, and the preservative is sucked into the timber cells by their partial vacuum. This method is ideal for timbers which are to be used in wet locations, e.g. marine work, docks, piers, jetties, etc. as water cannot penetrate into the timbers cells because they are already full of preservative.

Timber-based manufactured boards

The main types of timber-based manufactured boards used in the woodworking and building industries are:

Plywoods
Laminated boards (lamin, block and batten boards)
Chipboard (particle board)
Fibreboards

Plywoods

These consist of an odd number of thin layers of timber with their grains alternating across and along the panel or sheet. These are then glued together to form a strong board which will retain its shape and not have a tendency to shrink, expand or distort.

Plywood is manufactured in panel sizes varying from 1220 × 1220 mm up to 1525 × 3660 mm and thicknesses varying from 3 mm to 25 mm. Plywoods are available with various types of surface, according to the job they will be used for. They

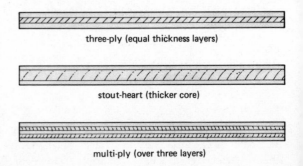

three-ply (equal thickness layers)

stout-heart (thicker core)

multi-ply (over three layers)

Figure 132   *Types of plywood*

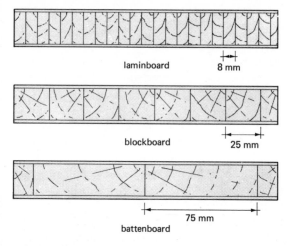

laminboard   8 mm

blockboard   25 mm

75 mm

battenboard

Figure 133   *Laminated boards*

are also graded according to the type of adhesive used in manufacture. INT, interior grade, will not withstand humidity or dampness. MR, moisture resistant and BR, boil resistant, are suitable for use under normal conditions, but will not withstand continuous exposure to extreme conditions. WBP plywoods, weather and boil proof, are suitable for use under any conditions.

Figure 132 shows three types of plywood:

Three-ply, which consists of three equal thickness layers.

Stout-heart, which also consists of three layers, but the middle layer is thicker.

Multi-ply, which is the name given to any plywood which has more than three layers.

Laminated boards (Figure 133)

These consist of strips of wood which are laminated together and sandwiched between two veneers. The width of the strips vary with each type of board. Laminboard has strips which are up to 8 mm in width; in blockboard these are up to 25 mm; and in battenboard up to 75 mm. All laminated boards are available in the same panel sizes as plywood. Thicknesses vary between 12 mm and 38 mm.

Chipboard

This is manufactured mostly from softwoods and is also known as particle board. It is made up of a

mixture of wood chips and wood flakes which are impregnated with resin. They are then pressed to form a flat, smooth-surfaced board. There is a wide range of panel sizes to suit particular requirements. Thicknesses vary between 9 mm and 30 mm.

Fibreboards

These include hardboards and insulating boards. They are manufactured from pulped wood which is mixed with an adhesive and pressed into sheets to the required thickness. They are available in a wide range of panel sizes up to 1220 × 5490 mm. Thicknesses vary between 2 mm and 12 mm for hardboard and between 9 mm and 25 mm for insulating board.

Adhesives

There is currently a vast range of adhesives which are available for use in the building industry. But it must be remembered that each adhesive has its own specific range of uses and that no one adhesive will satisfactorily bond all materials.

The main types of adhesive used in the woodworking industry are described below.

Animal glue

Animal glue is also known as scotch glue. It is made from animal hides and bones, but it is rarely used now, except in some small shops, because of the time taken to prepare it and its limitations. These glues are supplied in cake form and must be broken up, soaked and heated before use.

Casein adhesive

This adhesive is manufactured from soured, skimmed milk curds which are dried and crushed into a powder. An alkali and certain fillers are added to the powder to make it soluble in water and give it its gap-filling properties. Its main use is for general joinery although it is inclined to stain some hardwoods, particularly oak. Little preparation is required as the powder is simply mixed in a non-metal container with a measured quantity of cold water and stirred until a smooth creamy consistency is achieved.

Polyvinyl acetate glue

This is commonly known as PVA glue and is a thermo-plastic adhesive which is widely used for furniture and internal joinery. No preparation is required as this adhesive is usually supplied as a white creamy liquid in a nozzled polythene bottle. It does not stain timber, but some types can affect ferrous metal. PVA glue is one glue that does not blunt the cutting edge of tools.

Contact adhesive

This is a rubber-based adhesive which is supplied ready for use. It is mainly used for bonding plastic laminates and sheet floor covering. The adhesive must be applied to both surfaces and allowed to become touch dry before being brought together. This normally takes between ten and thirty minutes, depending on the make used. Once the two surfaces touch, no further movement or adjustment is normally possible, as an immediate contact or impact bond is obtained. Some types are available which allow a limited amount of adjustment to be made after contact.

Note: Care must be taken to use contact adhesives in a well ventilated area, where no smoking or naked lights are allowed.

Synthetic resin adhesives

These consist of three main types.

Phenol formaldehyde

This is classed as a WBP (weather and boil proof) adhesive. This means that it has a very high resistance to all weather conditions, cold and boiling water, micro-organisms, dry heat and steam. It is sold in two parts, the resin and the hardener, which are mixed together as required. A disadvantage of this type is that it normally requires a very high temperature in order to set. It is mainly used for exterior plywood, exterior joinery and timber engineering.

Resorcinol formaldehyde

This is completely water resistant and, like phenol formaldehyde, is classed as a WBP adhesive. It is sold as a liquid to which a powder or liquid hardener is added. It is mainly used for timber engineering and marine work.

Urea formaldehyde

This is classed as an MR (moisture resistant) adhesive. This means that it is moderately weather resistant and will withstand prolonged exposure to cold water, but very little to hot water. It is also resistant to micro-organisms. If urea formaldehyde is fortified by including resorcinol or melamine in the hardener, it can be classed as a BR (boil resistant) adhesive. This means that it has a good resistance to boiling water and fairly good weather resisting properties. It is also resistant to cold water and micro-organisms. Urea formaldehyde is available as either a one part adhesive that is mixed with water or as a two part adhesive with a separate hardener. Its main uses are for general joinery, furniture and plywood.

Table 4 shows the main uses and characteristics of these adhesives.

Notes:

Storage life refers to the period in which the materials forming the glue can be stored and still remain usable. After being stored for a certain length of time, glue becomes useless. This time varies with different types of glue. All glues should be stored in cool frost-free conditions.

Pot life refers to the time available for using the glue after it has been mixed. After a certain amount of time most glues become too thick to work with ease. Pot life and setting time depends to a large extent on the temperature.

Gap filling refers to adhesives that are capable of filling gaps up to 1.3 mm wide without affecting the strength of the joint.

Mastics

These are rubber- or plastic-based sealing compounds, which are used in modern buildings to seal joints around the outside of windows and door frames, against rain, air and sound, while still allowing differential movement between the two materials. These mastics are normally sold in tubes for use in guns which have a nozzle at one end through which the mastic is extruded.

Main uses and characteristics of woodworking adhesives

Type	Uses	Storage life	Pot life	Gap filling	Resistance to moisture
Animal glue (scotch)	General internal joinery (now largely replaced by other adhesives)	1 year +	Weeks if re-heated	Yes	None
Casein adhesive	General internal joinery and furniture (not recommended for use with certain hardwoods because of staining)	2 years +	Between 2 hours and 24 hours	Yes	Poor: can be improved by additives
Polyvinyl acetate (PVA) adhesive	General internal joinery and furniture	1 year	Months if not left open	No	Very poor
Contact adhesive	Bonding plastic laminates and sheet floor covering	1 year	Months if not left open	No	Fair
Phenol formaldehyde	External joinery, external plywood and timber engineering	1 year	Between 24 hours and 48 hours	No	WBP good
Resorcinol formaldehyde	Timber engineering and marine work	1 year	Between 2 hours and 4 hours	Yes	WBP very good
Urea formaldehyde	General joinery, furniture, plywood, fibreboard and chipboard	3 months to 1 year	Between ½ hour and 24 hours	Can be	MR or BR fairly good

Table 4

Ironmongery

The majority of ironmongery used by the carpenter and joiner can be classified into one of three groups which are as follows:

1 Fixing devices, e.g. nails, screws, bolts and plugs, etc.
2 Fittings which allow movement e.g. pivots, hinges and springs, etc.
3 Fittings which give security, e.g. locks, bolts, fasteners and stays, etc.

Note: Only basic items of ironmongery are covered in this chapter; further items are considered in *Carpentry and Joinery for Building Craft Students 2.*

Group 1

Nails
Nailing is the simplest way of joining pieces of wood together and to other materials. If carried out correctly it can result in a strong, lasting joint.

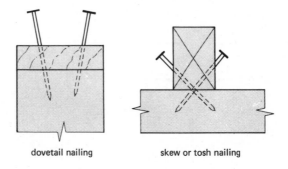

dovetail nailing   skew or tosh nailing

Figure 134   *Nailing for strength*

Hints on nailing
Where extra strength is required always dovetail or skew nail as shown in Figure 134. Using this method prevents the nails from being pulled out or working loose.

Where oval or rectangular section nails are used, the widest dimension must be parallel to the grain of the timber. (Their use in the opposite direction, across the grain, will normally result in the timber splitting.)

When nailing near the end of a piece of timber, the timber has a tendency to split. In order to overcome this, the point of the nail should be tapped with a hammer to blunt the point before the nail is used.

Note: The point of a nail tends to part the fibres of the timber and therefore split it, while the blunted end tends to tear its way through the fibres, making a large hole for itself.

Figure 135 shows a number of different types of nail which are commonly used.

The *wire nail*. These are also known as french nails and normally available in lengths from 12 mm to 150 mm. They are round in section and the larger sizes normally have a chequered head to reduce any possibility of the hammer slipping while the nail is being driven in. The top part of the shank is roughened to give the nail extra grip

in the timber. These are general purpose carpentry nails which can be used for all rough work where the presence of the nail head on the surface of the timber is not important, e.g. most carcassing, first fixing and formwork.

The *oval nail*. These, as the name implies, are oval in section and are available in lengths from 12 mm to 150 mm. They have a small head which can be punched below the surface. This is an advantage when fixing timber that has to be painted because the hole when filled is not visible.

The *cut nail*. These nails are cut from mild sheet steel and are square in section which gives a good grip. They are normally available up to 100 mm in length. The cut nail can be used for general construction work, but nowadays it is mainly used for fixing timber to blockwork walls, etc. They can also be used for nailing into the mortar joints of green (freshly laid) brickwork.

The *floor brad*. These are similar to the cut nail, but they are of a lighter section. They are available in lengths up to 75 mm and are used for the surface fixing of floor boards.

The *lost-head nail*. These are similar to the wire nail, but they have a small head which can be easily punched below the surface of the timber without making a large hole. Hence the name 'lost head'. They are used for fixing timber that has to be painted and also for the secret fixing of tongued and grooved flooring boards. They are available in lengths up to 75 mm.

The *panel pin*. These are a much lighter version of the lost-head nail and are used for fixing fine moulding around panels, etc. They are normally available in lengths between 12 mm and 50 mm.

The *annular nail*. These are a wire nail with a ringed shank, they can be hammered in easily but have the holding power of a screw. They can be used for all construction work where extra holding power is required. They are available in lengths up to 75 mm.

The *plasterboard nail*. These are galvanized to prevent them rusting, and they have a jagged shank for extra grip. They are available in lengths up to 40 mm and can be used to fix plasterboard and insulating board to timber ceiling joists, studwork and battens, etc.

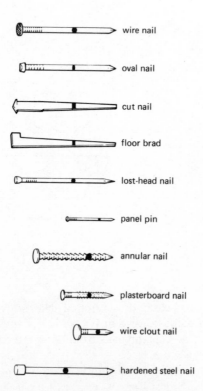

Figure 135   *Types of nail in common use*

The *wire clout nail*. These are a short galvanized wire nail with a large head. Their main use is for fixing roofing felt and building paper, etc. They are available in lengths between 12 mm and 25 mm.

The *hardened steel nail*. These are similar to the lost head nail but are made from a specially hardened zinc-plated steel for making hammered fixings directly into brickwork and concrete without plugging. They are available in lengths up to 100 mm.

Screws

In general a screwed joint is stronger than a nailed one and has the advantage of being easily removed and replaced when required.

All ironmongery such as locks, hinges, handles, fasteners and stays, etc., should be fixed using the appropriate screws. The main types of screw in common use are shown in Figure 136.

The *countersunk-head screw*. These are manufactured in either steel or brass and are available self-coloured or zinc or chromium plated. Countersunk screws are used for general purpose work where the screw is required to finish flush with the surface of the material.

The *round-head screw*. These are made from steel and have a black japanned finish to prevent them from rusting. They are mainly used for fixing tee hinges, barrel bolts, Suffolk latches and other similar black finished ironmongery.

The *raised-head screw*. These are normally used in conjunction with cups for good quality work where the screws are visible or where they might have to be removed from time to time, e.g. glazing beads and cabinet work, etc. They are also used for fixing lever furniture tower bolts and other similar ironmongery.

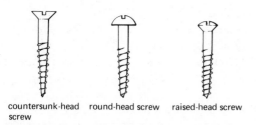

countersunk-head screw   round-head screw   raised-head screw

Figure 136   *Main types of screw*

The *coach screw*. These are used for heavy duty fixings to timber and, unlike other screws, they must be turned using a spanner.

The *'twin fast' screw*. These are used for screwing into all types of particle board where extra threads are needed to give the required grip.

Plugs

There are three different types of plug for screwing into.

A *common fibre plug*. Its use has now been largely superseded by the plastic plug.

A *plastic plug*. This has ridged edges for extra grip.

A *non-ferrous metal plug*. For use in damp or heat situations where fibre or plastic plugs are not suitable.

Hints for making screwed fixings into walls, etc.
It is most important to use the same size masonry drill, screw and plug.

The length of the plug should be the same as the threaded portion of the screw. If the unthreaded shank of the screw is turned into the plug, there is a good chance of the screw turning off or breaking off in the plug.

The drilled hole should be of such a depth that the plug is fully into the brick or blockwork and not the plaster, otherwise a weak fixing will result and there is a likelihood of the plaster pushing away from the wall around the hole.

The length of the screw should be selected so that it does not touch the bottom of the hole.

Hints for screwing into timber
Where two pieces of timber are to be screwed together, drill a hole through one piece equal to the diameter of the screw and countersink it if required.

A bradawl can be used to form a pilot hole to give a start to the screw in the other piece of timber.

When screwing into hardwood, the pilot hole should be drilled the full depth of the threaded portion of the screw.

Many carpenters and joiners rub tallow or candle wax on to the threaded portion of the screw to ease its insertion. This is especially useful when working with hardwood.

Group 2

Tee hinge (Figure 137)

These are mainly used for hanging ledged and braced doors and gates. This type of hinge is screwed directly onto the door and frame or post with black japanned round-head screws.

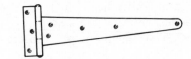

Figure 137   *Tee hinge*

Steel hook and band (Figure 138)

These are used for hanging heavyweight framed, ledged and braced doors, e.g. side-hung garage doors, etc. The band is bolted to the door and the hook is screwed to the frame.

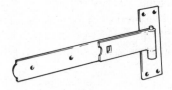

Figure 138   *Steel hook and band*

Butt hinge (Figure 139)

These can be manufactured from either mild steel, cast iron or brass, and are used for hanging cupboard doors, internal doors, external doors and traditional casement windows. For hanging cupboard doors and traditional casements, one pair of 38 mm, 50 mm or 63 mm hinges should be used. The size used will depend upon the weight of the door or window. In general the heavier the item the larger the hinge should be. Lightweight internal doors require one pair of 75 mm hinges, while glazed and heavier weight doors need one pair of 100 mm hinges. All external doors require one and a half pairs of 100 mm hinges.

Figure 139   *Butt hinge*

Note: Hardwood doors should be hung using brass or non-ferrous metal hinges, screws and other ironmongery. This is for two main reasons:

1   Many hardwoods, particularly oak, contain certain acids which cause steel fittings to rust and the timber develops a black stain around the steel fitting.
    Note: Cedar, although a softwood has the same effect on steel, therefore only non-ferrous metal fixings should be used with this timber as well.
2   For appearance. Polished brass fittings blend in with, and complement polished hardwood thereby providing a higher quality finish.

Offset hinge (Figure 140)

These are used for hanging casement windows. When open they allow an arm to be passed

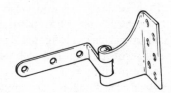

Figure 140   *Offset hinge*

through the gap between the frame and the casement in order to clean the outside of the window from the inside. Hence the name 'easy clean' hinge.

Group 3

The following items of ironmongery are suitable for ledged and braced doors and gates.

Thumb latch (Figure 141)

The thumb latch is also known as a Norfolk or Suffolk latch and is used to keep doors and gates closed. It may be operated from either side of the door, but provides no security on its own.

Padlock and hasp and staple (Figure 142)

These are used on external doors such as sheds and site huts, to provide a certain amount of

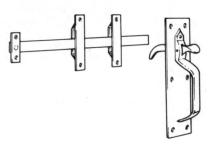

Figure 141   *Thumb latch*

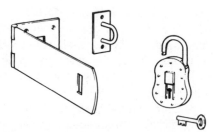

Figure 142   *Padlock and hasp and staple*

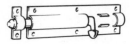

Figure 143   *Barrel bolt*

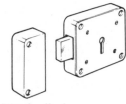

Figure 144   *Rim deadlock*

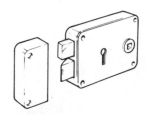

Figure 145   *Rimlock and latch*

Figure 146   *Knob furniture*

Figure 147   *Keyhole escutcheon plate*

security. The hasp is fixed to the door and the staple to the frame. Larger types are fixed by bolting through the door, rather than screwing, to provide greater protection.

Barrel bolts (Figure 143)
These are used on external doors and gates to lock them from the inside. Two bolts are normally used, one at the top of the door and the other at the bottom.

Rim deadlock (Figure 144)
The rim deadlock is normally used in place of barrel bolts or a padlock and hasp and staple. It has an advantage over both of these because it can be locked using a key, from either side of the door.

Rimlock and latch and knob furniture (Figures 145 and 146)
As this is a combined lock and latch, it does away with the necessity of using a thumb latch, padlock and hasp and staple or barrel bolts. It also gives the advantage, like the rim deadlock, of being able to lock the door using a key from either side.

Keyhole escutcheon plate (Figure 147)
This is used to provide a neat finish to the keyhole on both the rim deadlock and the rimlock and latch.

The following items of ironmongery are suitable for use on casement windows.

Casement stay (Figure 148)
This is also known as a peg stay. It is used to hold the window in various opening positions.

Figure 148   *Casement stay*

Figure 149   *Casement fastener*

Casement fastener (Figure 149)
This is also known as a cock spur and is used to secure a casement window in the closed position.

Concrete

While the carpenter and joiner is not usually directly involved with concrete, a basic knowledge of its composition is desired.

Concrete is composed of four materials.

Portland cement
Fine aggregate (sand)
Coarse aggregate (stones)
Water

When these materials are mixed together, the fine aggregate fills the voids in between the coarse aggregate. The cement mixes with the water and coats the surfaces of the aggregate, bonding them together. The concrete then sets by a chemical reaction between the cement and the water.

Concrete mixes
Concrete mixes are normally specified by volume. A typical specified mix might be 1:3:6. This means:
1 part Portland cement
3 parts fine aggregate
6 parts coarse aggregate

The amount of water used in the mix should be kept to the minimum required to provide a workable mix. This is because, as the amount of water increases above the minimum, the strength of the concrete decreases.

Concrete rapidly increases in strength during its initial curing process (setting). It will have obtained 85 per cent of its strength after twenty-eight days, and will continue to gain the remaining 15 per cent of its strength during the rest of its life.

It is important that the concrete cures under the correct conditions. If its moisture dries out too quickly, the chemical reaction between the cement and water will be retarded, resulting in a weaker concrete. This is why freshly laid concrete is often covered during hot weather with plastic sheets or wet sacking.

Concrete is an extremely strong material. Its main strength is in compression, e.g. when used in columns and pillars, etc. When used in tension, e.g. beams and lintels, it should be reinforced with steel to increase or reinforce its strength.

Self-assessment questions

1 The method of applying timber preservative that attains the deepest penetration is
   (a) spraying
   (b) dipping
   (c) pressure impregnation
   (d) brushing

2 When plywood is marked WBP this indicates that it is
   (a) water and boil proof
   (b) weather and boil proof
   (c) water and burn proof
   (d) weather and burn proof

3 Radially sawn timber can be defined as having growth rings which meet the face of the timber at an angle of
   (a) more than 45 degrees
   (b) less than 45 degrees
   (c) more than 30 degrees
   (d) less than 30 degrees

4 A concrete mix of 1:3:6 means that it is mixed using the following proportions
   (a) cement, fine aggregate, coarse aggregate
   (b) cement, coarse aggregate, water
   (c) fine aggregate, coarse aggregate, cement
   (d) water, cement, fine aggregate

5 The timber which is most commonly used for carpentry is
   (a) oak
   (b) parana pine
   (c) spruce
   (d) European redwood

6 The moisture content of timber that is known as the dry rot safety line is
   (a) 15 per cent
   (b) 20 per cent
   (c) 25 per cent
   (d) 30 per cent

7 When eradicating an attack of dry rot, all affected timber should be
   (a) removed and immediately burnt on site
   (b) left in place and treated with a preservative
   (c) removed and placed in a builder's rubbish skip
   (d) removed and taken away to a refuse dump to be burnt

8 To which group of timber preservatives does creosote belong?
   (a) water-soluble
   (b) paint
   (c) organic solvents
   (d) tar oils

9 The actual cell-producing part of the tree is known as the
   (a) bark and bast
   (b) sapwood
   (c) cambium layer
   (d) medullary rays

10 The best nails to use when secret-fixing tongued and grooved floor boarding are
   (a) lost-head nails
   (b) wire nails
   (c) floor brads
   (d) galvanized clout nails

chapter 4

Basic woodworking joints

After reading this chapter you should be able to:

1 Identify and sketch basic woodworking joints.

2 Explain the principles involved in the construction of basic woodworking joints.

3 List the operations involved in making various basic woodworking joints.

4 Select the most suitable joint for a given situation.

Woodworking joints can be divided into three main groups:

Joints in length
Joints in width
Angle joints

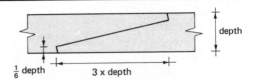

Figure 151   *Scarf joint for wide board*

Joints in length

This type of joint is used where the required length of timber is not available, or where short lengths of timber are used to save wastage. The four main types are described below.

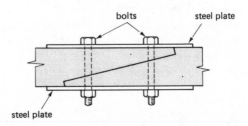

Figure 152   *Scarf joint bolted and plated*

Scarf joints

These joints are mainly used in carpentry work, e.g. for jointing wall plates (Figure 150). Figure 151 shows a scarf joint which is suitable for use on a wide board. Where additional strength is required (purlins and beams) scarf joints can be bolted and plated. See Figure 152.

Laminated joints

This method of jointing is used mainly to utilize short lengths of timber. It can also be used for making up curved or shaped work. Figure 153

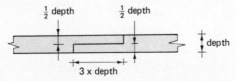

Figure 150   *Scarf joint for wall plate*

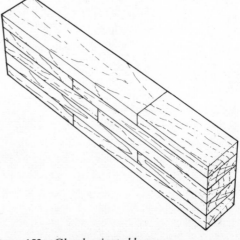

Figure 153   *Glue-laminated beam*

shows a glue-laminated beam used for structural work. Notice that the joints in length are staggered to obtain maximum strength. Figure 154 shows the head of a semicircular frame which has been glue-laminated from a number of separate pieces of timber.

Figure 154   *Head of a semicircular frame*

Heading joint
This joint is used when lengthening floor boards, skirtings and mouldings. Figure 155 shows a heading joint on a floor board.
Note: This joint must be placed over a floor joist. Figure 156 shows a heading joint in mid length of a piece of skirting.

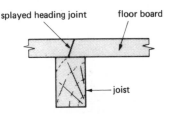

Figure 155   *Heading joint on a floor board*

Handrail bolt
This is mainly used by joiners for handrailing and intersections of bay window sills. The two pieces are butt jointed and held together with a handrail bolt. See Figure 157. The position of the bolt is carefully marked out and drilled. Two mortises are then cut to receive the nuts, one square which is inserted first, and the other round which is inserted and then tightened with a nail punch. The tightening of the nut draws the two ends of the timber close together. Short pieces of dowel rod are often used in conjunction with the bolt to resist the tendency of the joint to twist.

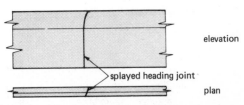

Figure 156   *Heading joint in mid length of skirting*

Joints in width

This type of joint enables narrow boards to be built up to cover large areas (floor boards, cladding, etc.), or built up to form wider boards for shelving, cabinet work, table tops, etc. Figure 158 shows a butt joint where the square edges of the pieces of timber are glued together.

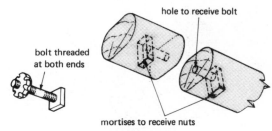

Figure 157   *Use of a handrail bolt*

Figure 159 is an improvement of the butt joint. Both sides are grooved out and a loose plywood tongue is inserted. It is mainly used for cabinet work and counter tops.

For flooring, a tongue and groove joint (T & G) is used. Figure 160 shows the section for surface nailing and Figure 161 for secret nailing (nailing through the tongue). Figure 162 shows tongued, grooved and vee-jointed boarding, (T, G & V or matchboarding). It is mainly used for

Figure 158   *Butt joint*

Figure 159   *Loose tongue*

Figure 160   *Tongue and groove (T & G) boarding: surface nailing*

Figure 161   *T & G boarding: secret nailing*

Figure 162   *T, G & V jointed (matchboarding)*

Figure 163   *Shiplap boarding*

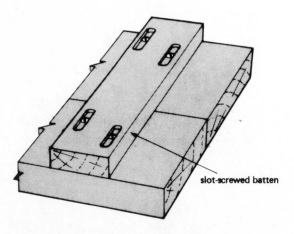

slot-screwed batten

Figure 164   *Use of slot-screwed batten*

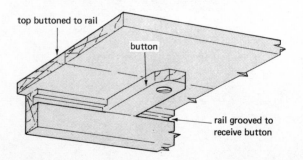

top buttoned to rail

button

rail grooved to
receive button

Figure 165   *Button*

cladding, panelling and external door or gate construction.

Another boarding used for cladding is shiplap. It is widely used for covering sheds, etc. See Figure 163.

When boards are joined to form wide tops, it is advisable to use slot-screwed battens on the underside. (Figure 164). The use of the slot-screwed batten stops the top from distorting while still allowing a certain amount of moisture movement in the top (shrinkage and expansion).

Figure 165 shows a button which is often used to secure counter tops and table tops in place. This method allows the top to expand and shrink without any distortion or splitting, as the buttons allow the top and legs to move independently of each other.

Angle joints

These cover a wide range. They are often termed framing joints and are used extensively by both the carpenter and joiner. The main types are:

The *mitre joint,* shown in Figure 166. The main uses are for mitring, skirting, architraves and mouldings.

The *half-lapped joint.* There are a number of variations of this type of joint, but the principle of each is the same. Half the thickness of timber is cut from each member and the joint is then held together by glue, screws or nails. Figures 167, 168 and 169 show a number of half-lapped joints.

The *dovetail joint* used mainly in box and drawer construction. Figure 170 shows through dovetails which are used for boxes and the backs of drawers. On the front of drawers lapped dovetails are used (Figure 171). These provide a neater finished appearance.

Housing joints

Square housing joint
This joint is used for two main purposes.

For *stud partitions,* shown in Figure 172. The joint would be secured with wire nails.

Note: The depth of the housing should not exceed one-third the thickness of the timber.

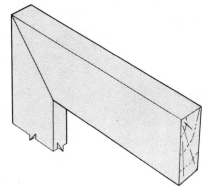

Figure 166   *Mitre joint*

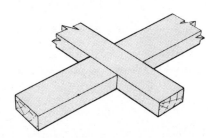

Figure 167   *Cross halving*

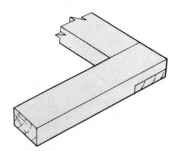

Figure 168   *Corner halving*

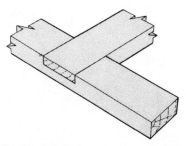

Figure 169   *Tee halving*

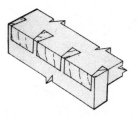

Figure 170   *Through dovetail joint*

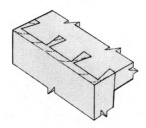

Figure 171   *Lapped dovetail joint*

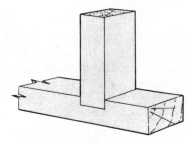

Figure 172   *Square housing joint used in stud partition*

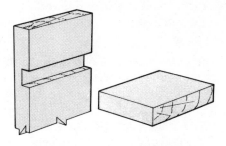

Figure 173   *Square housing joint used for fixing shelves*

For *fixing shelves* in cabinet work, where the joint would be glued and possibly screwed from the back of the housing. See Figure 173.

Stopped housing joint
This joint is an improvement of the square housing joint and is used for better quality cabinet

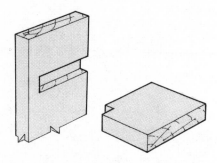

Figure 174   *Stopped housing joint*

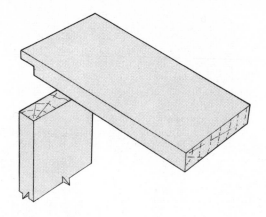

Figure 175   *Corner housing joint*

work. Figure 174 shows that the housing is stopped back from the face of the upright. This gives a neater appearance to the job.

Corner housing joint

This joint is often used for low-cost door linings and is shown in Figure 175. On better quality work, the shouldered housing joint would be used. This joint is shown in Figure 176. Both joints are secured by nailing through the head of the lining.

Mortise and tenon joint

This joint is probably the most widely used angle joint. It is used extensively for door and window construction and general framework. Figure 177 gives the two basic rules for all mortise and tenon joints.

1   The tenon should be one-third the thickness of the timber to be joined. If a chisel is not available to chop the mortise to receive the tenon, the thickness of the tenon may be adjusted to the nearest available chisel size.
2   The width of the tenon should not exceed five times its thickness. This is to overcome the tendency of a wide tenon to buckle and also to reduce the effect of shrinkage.

The tenon is glued and inserted into the mortise. Wedges are used to tighten and hold the joint. On jobs which are difficult to cramp, draw pins are used to draw up the shoulders of the joint. This joint is shown in Figure 178. Notice that the holes are drilled off-centre so that when the pin is driven in it has a tightening effect.

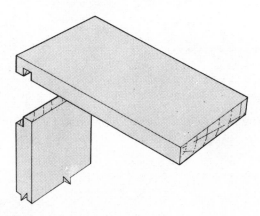

Figure 176   *Shoulder housing joint*

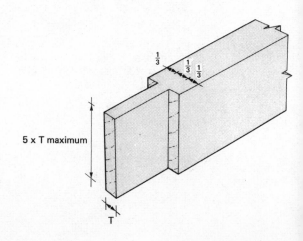

Figure 177   *Basic rules for mortise and tenon joints*

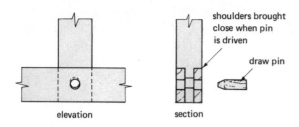

elevation   section

Figure 178   *Draw-pinning*

shoulders brought close when pin is driven

draw pin

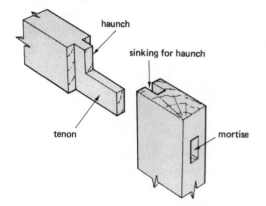

haunch

sinking for haunch

tenon

mortise

Figure 179   *Haunched mortise and tenon joint*

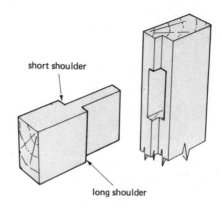

short shoulder

long shoulder

Figure 180   *Mortise and tenon in rebated timber*

Haunched mortise and tenons

Where the width of the tenon would exceed five times its thickness or where the joint is at the end of a piece of framework, a haunched mortise and tenon is used. The use of the haunch reduces the width of the tenon and enables it to be wedged without any appreciable loss in strength. This joint is mainly used in door construction. Figure 179 shows a haunched mortise and tenon joint.

The following should be noted when making haunched mortise and tenon joints in softwoods. The width of the tenon should be divided into two, half for the haunch and half for the tenon. In hardwoods the width of the tenon should be divided into three, one-third for the haunch and two-thirds for the tenon.

Mortise and tenons in moulded timber

When the two pieces to be jointed are rebated on one edge, the shoulder lines will be stepped (long and short shoulders). This is shown in Figure 180. When moulded sections are jointed the moulding must be either scribed or mitred.

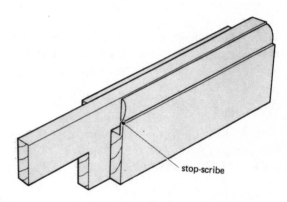

stop-scribe

Figure 181   *Stop-scribed joint*

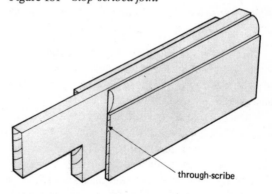

through-scribe

Figure 182   *Through-scribed joint*

Figure 181 shows a joint which is stop-scribed. This is the hand method of scribing a moulding.

Figure 182 shows a joint which is through-scribed. This is the machine method of scribing a moulding.

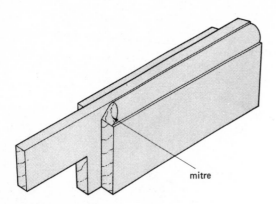

Figure 183   *Mitred moulding*

Figure 183 shows a joint where the moulding has been mitred. This can only be carried out by hand.

Preparing timber

The first operation in making an item of joinery is the sawing of the timber to the required size. This involves two operations:

Cross-cutting to length.
Ripping to the required section.

Note: The saw cut should always be on the waste side of the line.

Care should be taken not to use timber with large defects, e.g. knots, shakes etc. By careful selection and cutting, these defects can normally be avoided.

Once sawn to the required section, the timber should then be planed. The object of this is to obtain a flat, true and smooth surface.
Note: 5 mm is normally allowed on sawn sizes for planing up. This gives 2.5 mm on each surface of the timber to be planed off. There are four operations involved in planing up. These are:

1 Using a jack or trying plane, plane face side straight and out of twist, then mark face side.
   Note: Winding sticks are used to check for twist. One should sight from one end. When the tops of the winding sticks are parallel the timber is out of twist (out of wind).

2 Plane the face edge true and square to the face side. Check with try square. Mark face edge.
3 Set gauge to width and mark timber. Plane timber to width.
4 Set gauge to thickness and mark timber. Plane timber to thickness.

Cutting joints
When all sawing and planing operations have been completed, the marking out and cutting of the joints can be started. Details of cutting three basic joints are given in this chapter:

Halving joint
Dovetail joint
Mortise and tenon joint

Halving joint
The operations involved in making the various types of halving joints are all very similar. The sequence given is for the tee halving joint.

1 Mark out.
   Note: Half the thickness of timber is marked with the marking gauge.
2 Saw down the centre of the cross rail, then cut the shoulder.
3 Cut the other half of the joint. This is done in two stages.
   (a) Cut the two edges of the joint and make a further saw cut in the centre.
   (b) Using a chisel cut away the waste and pare down to the gauge line.
4 Assemble joint.

These operations are shown in Figure 184.

Dovetail joint
Dovetail joints should have a pitch or slope of one in six for softwood and one in seven for hardwood. This can be marked out using a dovetail template or a sliding bevel. If the sliding bevel is used it can be set up as shown in Figure 185.

The operations involved in making a dovetail joint for wide boards are:

1 Mark out sockets.
2 Cut the sockets with a fine tenon saw.
3 Mark the pins from the sockets.

4 Cut the pins with a fine tenon saw. (As in number 2.)
5 Remove the waste with a chisel.
6 Assemble the joint.

These operations are shown in Figure 186.

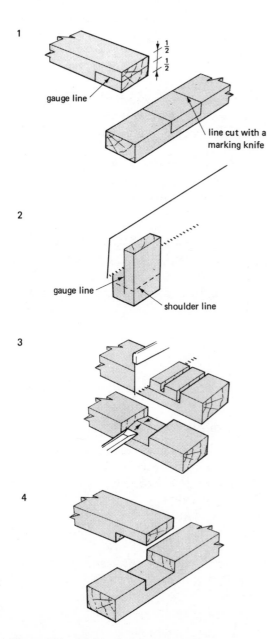

Figure 184 *Making halving joints*

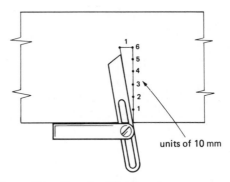

Figure 185 *Use of a sliding bevel*

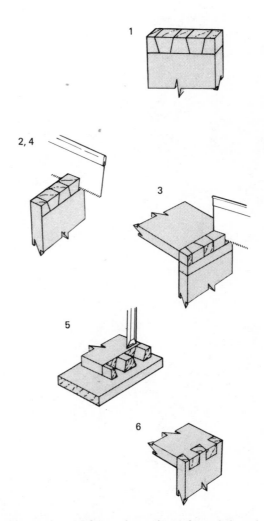

Figure 186 *Making a dovetail joint for wide boards*

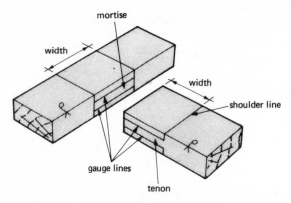

Figure 187 *Marking out timber for a mortise and tenon joint*

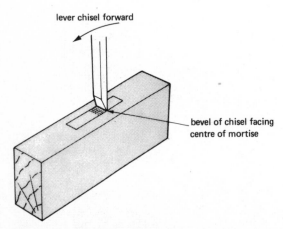

Figure 188 *Mortise from the back edge of the timber*

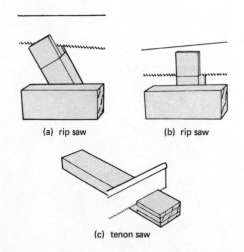

Figure 189 *Cutting the tenons*

Mortise and tenon joint

The operations involved in making a mortise and tenon joint are:

1   Mark out timber. Gauge mortise and tenons with the marking gauge. Mark the shoulder line with a marking knife. See Figure 187.
Note: The gauge should be set to the chisel size.

2   Chop the mortise. This is done in three stages.
(a) Mortise from the back edge of the timber using a mortise chisel. See Figure 188.
(b) Complete the mortise from the face edge of the timber.
(c) Cut mortises to receive wedges on the back edge of the timber.

3   Cut the tenons. This is also done in three stages.
(a) Rip the tenon from both sides with the timber in a sloping position.
(b) Complete the cuts with the timber in an upright position.
(c) Cut the shoulders.
Note: The shoulders should not be cut until all the required moulding operations have been carried out.
These stages are shown in Figure 189.

4   Fit joint.

Self-assessment questions

1   A ridge board requires lengthening. The most suitable joint to use would be a
(a) mortise and tenon joint
(b) dovetail joint
(c) scarf joint
(d) heading joint

2   A dovetail joint is to be made in softwood. The slope or pitch of the pins should be
(a) 1 in 7
(b) 1 in 5
(c) 1 in 6
(d) 2 in 6

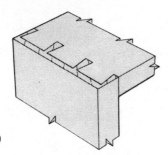

Figure 190

3 The joint illustrated in Figure 190 is a
   (a) mortise and tenon joint
   (b) dovetail joint
   (c) haunched mortise and tenon joint
   (d) lapped dovetail joint

4 When making housing joints, the depth of the joint should not exceed
   (a) half the thickness of the timber
   (b) one-quarter the thickness of the timber
   (c) one-third the thickness of the timber
   (d) two-thirds the thickness of the timber

5 When preparing sawn timber, there are four operations which must be carried out:
   (1) planing to width
   (2) planing to thickness
   (3) planing face side
   (4) planing face edge
   The correct sequence for planing the timber would be
   (a) 2, 1, 3, 4
   (b) 3, 4, 1, 2
   (c) 3, 1, 2, 4
   (d) 4, 3, 2, 1

6 A button can be used to secure
   (a) mortise and tenon joints
   (b) table tops
   (c) hand rails
   (d) shiplap boarding

7 The joint shown in Figure 190 is mainly used for
   (a) box construction
   (b) frame construction
   (c) backs of drawers
   (d) fronts of drawers

8 When cutting haunched mortise and tenon joints in softwood, the proportions of the joint should be
   (a) half haunch, half tenon
   (b) quarter haunch, three-quarter tenon
   (c) third haunch, two-third tenon
   (d) two-third haunch, third tenon

9 The most suitable joint for lengthening a wall plate would be a
   (a) butt joint
   (b) heading joint
   (c) laminated joint
   (d) scarf joint

10 Only two of the following statements are correct.
   (1) A mortise and tenon joint is classed as a framing joint.
   (2) Matchboarding is another name for tongued, grooved and vee-jointed boarding.
   (3) The width of a tenon should not exceed three times its thickness.
   (4) A handrail bolt joint is only suitable for joining handrails.
   Which are they?
   (a) 1 and 3
   (b) 3 and 4
   (c) 4 and 2
   (d) 2 and 1

chapter 5

Joinery

After reading this chapter you should be able to:

1 List a suitable sequence of operations for the making of joinery items.

2 Recognize various items of joinery.

3 Prepare sketches to show various joinery details.

4 Select the most suitable item of joinery for a given purpose.

5 List a suitable sequence of operations involved in the hanging of casements and cupboard doors.

6 Explain and illustrate the principles of rod making.

Doors

Timber doors may be classified into one of the following groups:

Panelled and glazed doors
Flush doors
Fire-check doors
Matchboarded doors

The first three of these groups are not dealt with in this chapter, but are covered fully in *Carpentry and Joinery for Building Craft Students 2*.

Matchboarded doors

This group of doors involves the simplest form of construction. They can be used both internally and externally, although they are mainly used for gates, sheds and outhouses.

The basic door consists of matchboarding which is held together by ledges. This type is little used because it has a tendency to sag and distort on the side opposite the hinges. In order to overcome this braces are incorporated in the construction. The use of the braces greatly increases the rigidity of the door.

Shown in Figure 191 is the rear elevation and sections of a ledged and matchboarded door.
Note: Where these doors are used externally, the top edge of the ledges should be chamfered. This is done to stop the accumulation of rainwater and moisture.

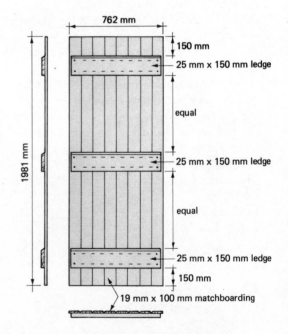

Figure 191   *Ledged and matchboarded door*

A ledged, braced and matchboarded door is shown in Figure 192.
Note: The bottom ends of the braces should always point towards the hinged edge of the door. This is most important because if the braces slope in the wrong direction, they will increase instead of decrease the tendency for the door to sag.

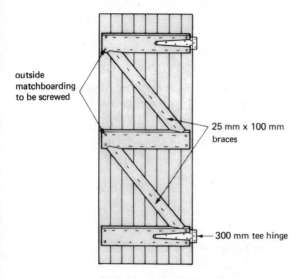

outside matchboarding to be screwed

25 mm x 100 mm braces

300 mm tee hinge

Figure 192   *Ledged, braced and matchboarded door*

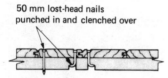

50 mm lost-head nails punched in and clenched over

Figure 193   *Clenching over*

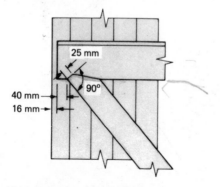

25 mm

90°

40 mm

16 mm

Figure 194   *Joint detail between ledges and braces*

Three ledges are used to hold the matchboarding together. The outside pieces should be fixed with screws, the remaining lengths of matchboarding are nailed to the ledges. Lost-head nails 6 mm longer than the thickness of the door are used for this purpose. The nails should be punched in and clenched over. Clenching over

simply means bending the protruding part of the nails over and punching the ends below the surface. This is shown in Figure 193.

The two braces, when used, are also fixed with lost-head nails which are clenched over. The joint detail between the ledges and braces is shown in Figure 194.

Before the door is assembled all concealed surfaces, such as the tongues and grooves of the matchboarding and the backs of the ledges and braces, should be painted with a priming paint. This is in order to prevent moisture penetration and subsequent rotting of the timber which may occur if this operation is not carried out.

All doors including matchboarded doors are produced in a standard range of sizes and should be available from most joinery manufacturers.

Door frames and linings

Doors can be hung on either frames or linings, which are built in, or fixed into an opening in a wall or partition.

Door frames are made from rectangular section timber into which a 12 mm rebate is cut to receive the door. Frames should be used for all external doors and heavy internal doors. See Figure 195.

Door linings are made from 25 mm or 32 mm boards which cover the full width of the wall, including the plaster. Planted door stops (nailed on) are normally used to accomodate the door. Architraves are fixed around the door lining to cover the joint between the plaster and the wood.

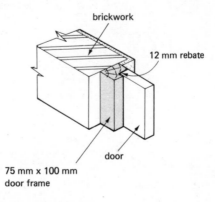

brickwork

12 mm rebate

door

75 mm x 100 mm door frame

Figure 195   *Door frame*

Door linings are used for the majority of internal doors. See Figure 196. In this chapter only door frames are considered. Door linings being covered in *Carpentry and Joinery for Building Craft Students 2*.

A door frame consists of three or four components. These are the head, two jambs and, where used, a sill or threshold. The components

are joined together with draw-pinned mortise and tenon joints. The joint between the head and the jamb is shown in Figure 197. A typical hardwood threshold section is shown in Figure 198.

Note: All joints should be coated with a suitable priming paint before assembly.

Door frames are normally built into the brickwork as the work proceeds. Temporary struts are used to hold the frame upright, while the foot of the jambs are held in position by galvanized metal dowels which protrude from the jambs and are grouted into the concrete. This is shown in Figure 199.

Note: Temporary braces and distance pieces are fixed to the frame in order to keep the frame square and the jambs parallel during the 'building in' process.

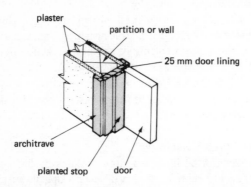

Figure 196   *Door lining*

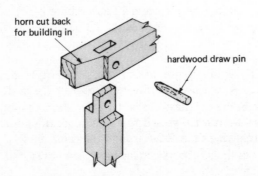

Figure 197   *Draw-pinned mortise and tenon joint*

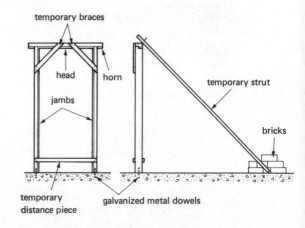

Figure 199   *'Building in' a frame*

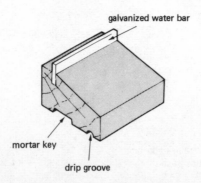

Figure 198   *Typical hardwood threshold section*

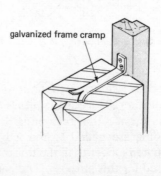

Figure 200   *Attaching frame cramps*

As the brickwork proceeds galvanized metal frame cramps should be screwed to the back of the jambs and built into the brickwork, as shown in Figure 200.

Three or four cramps should be evenly spaced up each jamb. The horns of the frame are normally cut back as shown in Figure 197 before 'building in'.

Windows

Windows are incorporated into buildings for three main reasons. These are:

To admit daylight into the building.
To admit air into the building. (This is a statutory requirement; see the Building Regulations Part K 4.)
To give the occupants of the building an outside view.

Windows are normally classified by their method of opening. The majority of windows come under one of the following three groups. These groups are illustrated in Figure 201.

1 Casements which are either top or side hung on hinges.
2 Pivot hung. These can be either horizontally or vertically hung.
3 Sliding sashes. These can slide either horizontally or vertically.

In this chapter only casement windows are considered. Pivot hung and sliding sash windows will be covered in *Carpentry and Joinery for Building Craft Students 2*.

Casement windows

The majority of houses built from the 1930s up to the present day incorporate this type of window. Houses constructed before the 1930s were normally built with vertical sliding sash windows.

Casement windows consist of two main parts.

The frame, which comprises the head, sill and jambs.
The casement, which comprises the top rail, bottom rail and stiles.

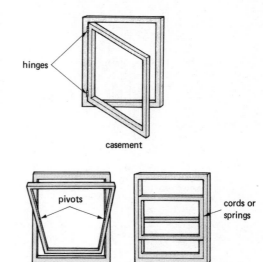

Figure 201 *Types of window*

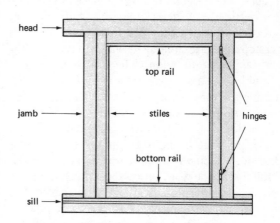

Figure 202 *Single-light casement window*

Illustrated in Figure 202 is a single-light casement window, with all its component parts named.

Casement windows can be further divided into two types.

Traditional casements, which are illustrated in Figure 203.
Stormproof casements, which are illustrated in Figure 204.

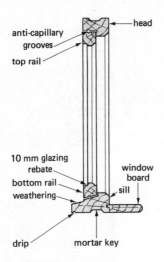

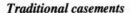

Figure 203   *Traditional casement*

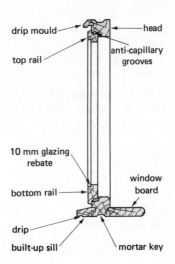

Figure 204   *Stormproof casement*

Traditional casements

In this type, the frame has a 12 mm rebate to receive the casement, which finishes flush with the outside of the head and jambs. Anti-capillary grooves are run around the frame and casement to stop rainwater finding its way into the building by capillary attraction. The sill of the frame should have a slope on its top surface, so that rainwater may easily run off. This is called weathering. A 6 mm drip groove is run along the underside of the sill, which causes the rainwater to 'drip off' at this point and not run back under the sill. Casement window frames are normally 'built in' as the work proceeds in much the same manner as door frames, two or three galvanized frame cramps being used on the back of each jamb. The mortar key also helps to hold the frame. This should be solidly filled with cement mortar as the brickwork proceeds.

Note: Capillary attraction is the phenomenon whereby water can travel against the force of gravity in fine spaces or between two surfaces which are close together. The smaller the space the greater will be the capillary attraction.

Stormproof casements

This type has now become the standard type of casement window. It incorporates two rebates, one around the frame and the other around the casement. The use of the two rebates and the anti-capillary grooves stop all rainwater, including wind-driven rain, finding its way into the building. A drip mould is used along the head of the frame to stop any rainwater running into the joint between the head and top rail. To save on the wastage of using large section timber, the sill is normally built up in two sections.

Joints

The jointing of the frame of both types of casement window is the same, the mortise and tenon joint being used throughout. This is shown in Figure 205. In the traditional frame, the joint is normally wedged, whereas the joint in the storm-proof frame is secured by a metal star dowel.

The jointing of the actual casement differs between the two types. The traditional casement uses a haunched mortise and tenon, which is secured with wedges. This is shown in Figure 206. The joint used for a stormproof casement is a comb joint which is secured with a metal star dowel. This is shown in Figure 207.

Before assembly, the joints of windows, like those of door frames, should be coated with a suitable priming paint.

Note: When synthetic resin adhesive is used it is not necessary to paint the joints of door and window frames before assembly.

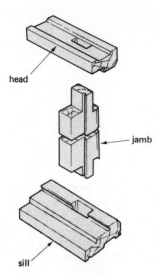

Figure 205   *Jointing the frame*

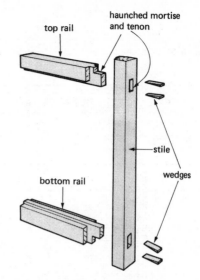

Figure 206   *Haunched mortise and tenon joint, secured with wedges*

Production of joinery items

When making any item of joinery, various stages of work have to be carried out in order to complete the job. By adopting a methodical approach great savings can be achieved, both in time and prevention of costly mistakes.

The following workshop procedure checklist can be used to great advantage in both the hand and mechanized joiner's shop.

Workshop checklist

1   Prepare rod and cutting list from scale drawing.
2   Select sawn timber from stock.
3   Plane timber on face sides.
4   Plane timber on face edges.
5   Plane timber to width.
6   Plane timber to thickness.
7   Mark out timber from rod.
8   Chop mortises.
9   Rip down the sides of the tenons.
10   Run square sections (rebates, plough grooves, etc.).
11   Run moulded sections.
12   Cut the shoulders of the tenons.
13   Fit the joints.
14   Assemble item dry. Check sizes, square and winding.

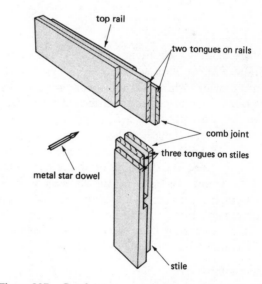

Figure 207   *Comb joint secured with a metal star dowel*

15   Clean up inside faces or edges of timber.
16   Glue up, re-check sizes, square and winding.
17   Clean up item.
18   Fit and hang any casements or cupboard doors.

Note: Stages 9 and 12 will, in mechanized shops, be carried out in one operation on a tenoning machine.

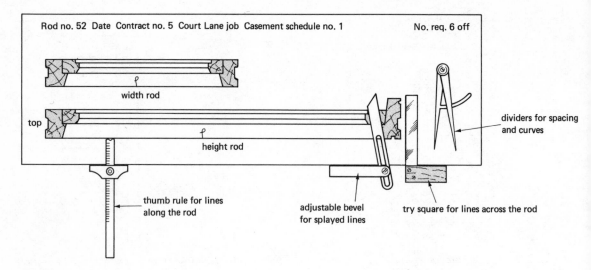

Figure 208   *Rod for a casement window*

Workshop rods
When making most items of joinery it is normal practice to set out a workshop rod. This is a full size drawing, which is usually done on thin plywood, or white-painted hardboard. However, simple, one-off jobs are often marked out directly on the timber, without using a rod.

A typical rod for a casement window is shown in Figure 208. The drawings on the rod show the sections and positions of the various window components on a height and width rod. All of the component parts of the window can then be marked accurately from the rod. The rod should also contain the following information:

Rod number
Date drawn
Contract number and location
The scale drawing from which the rod was produced
The number of jobs required

The drawing equipment the setter-out will use to produce the rod is also shown in Figure 208:
1   A thumb rule for lines along the rod
2   An adjustable bevel for splayed lines
3   A try square for lines across the rod
4   Dividers for spacing and curves

Note: The head, or top of the job, should be drawn on the left of the rod and the face of the job should be drawn nearest the setter-out.

Figure 209 shows the three easy stages which can be used to build up a detailed drawing. This method can be used when producing both workshop rods or scale drawings:

1   The components are drawn in their rectangular sections.
2   The square and moulded sections are added.
3   All other details are then added including hatching.

Note: The square and moulded sections should be the same depth. This eases the fitting of the joint as the shoulders of the tenon will be in the same position.

When the rod has been completed, a cutting list, which shows the finished sizes of all components, should be made. A cutting list for the casement window in the rod is shown in Figure 210.

Squaring up
The squareness of a frame is checked with a squaring rod. Figure 211 shows a typical squaring

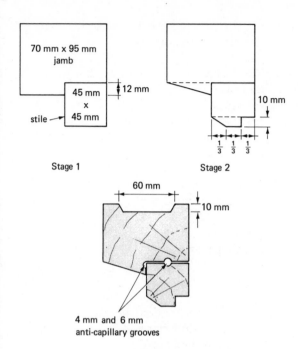

Stage 1

Stage 2

Stage 3

Figure 209   *Building up a drawing*

Cutting list		
Rod no. 52	Date	Contract no. 5
Job title	Casement window	
Item	No. off	Finished size (mm)
Frame:		
jambs	12	70 x 95 x 1000
head	6	70 x 95 x 700
sill	6	70 x 120 x 700
Casement:		
stiles	12	45 x 45 x 900
top rail	6	45 x 45 x 500
bottom rail	6	45 x 70 x 500

Figure 210   *Cutting list*

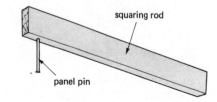

Figure 211   *Squaring rod*

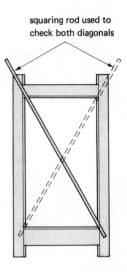

Figure 212   *Pulling the frame into square*

rod. It consists of a length of rectangular section timber, with a panel pin in its end. Figure 212 shows a squaring rod in use. The end with the panel pin is placed in one corner. The length of the diagonal should then be marked in pencil on the rod. The other diagonal should then be checked. If the pencil marks occur in the same place, the frame must be square. If the frame is not square, the sash cramps should be angled to pull the frame into square.

Casement and cupboard door hanging

Stormproof casements and many modern cupboard doors which fit on the face of a frame require no fitting at all. The only operation necessary to hang the casement or door is the screwing on of the hinges.

However, traditional casements and doors which fit inside the frame, require both fitting and hanging. This is often thought of as a difficult task, but by following the procedure given, the task is greatly simplified.

Fitting and hanging procedure

1   Mark the hanging side on both the door and the frame.

2   Cut off the horns.

3 'Shoot in' (plane to fit) the hanging stile.
4 Shoot the door to width.
5 'Shoot in' the top and the bottom of the door.
6 Mark out and cut in the hinges.
7 Screw one leaf of the hinges to the door.
8 Offer up the door to the opening and screw the other leaf to the frame.
9 Adjust fit if required and fix any other ironmongery.

Note: The two stiles when planed should have a 'leading edge' (slightly out of square). This allows the door to close freely without binding. The joint around cupboard doors should be 1 mm, but on casements the joint should be increased to 2 mm. This is because the casement is in an external position and will be liable to a certain amount of moisture movement.

Self-assessment questions

1 Braces are incorporated into matchboarded doors in order to
  (a) provide a fixing for the hinges
  (b) prevent the door from sagging
  (c) joint matchboarding together
  (d) protect the door from weather

2 Anti-capillary grooves are run around window frames and casements in order to
  (a) form a rebate to receive the opening casement
  (b) provide a moulding around the window
  (c) prevent wind entering the building
  (d) prevent rainwater entering the building

3 The length of the lost-head nails used to fix a 19 mm matchboarding to 25 mm ledges and braces of a ledged, braced and matchboarded door should be
  (a) 40 mm
  (b) 30 mm
  (c) 35 mm
  (d) 50 mm

4 A rectangular frame can be 'squared' by
  (a) using winding sticks
  (b) checking that the sides are parallel

  (c) checking that the diagonals are equal
  (d) using a large set square

5 The vertical members in a window frame are known as
  (a) stiles
  (b) posts
  (c) uprights
  (d) jambs

6 When making a window frame, the operation to be carried out directly after planing should be
  (a) mark out timber
  (b) chop mortises
  (c) rip sides of tenons
  (d) prepare rod

7 What has been omitted from Figure 213 which would result in water finding its way into the inside of the building?
  (a) mortar key
  (b) drip mould
  (c) anti-capillary groove
  (d) drip groove

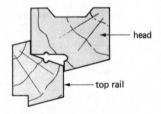

Figure 213   *Self-assessment question*

8 When hanging a cupboard door the fitting stages are:
  (1) shoot to width
  (2) shoot hanging stile
  (3) plane top and bottom
  (4) cut off horns
  The correct sequence of these stages should be
  (a) 4, 2, 1, 3
  (b) 4, 1, 2, 3
  (c) 1, 2, 3, 4
  (d) 2, 4, 1, 3

9 The normal joint used for a stormproof casement is a
   (a) draw-pinned mortise and tenon
   (b) mortise and tenon with star dowel
   (c) draw-pinned comb joint
   (d) comb joint with star dowel

10 Which one of the window sections shown in
   Figure 214 will give the most effective
   weather protection?
   (a) 1
   (b) 2
   (c) 3
   (d) 4

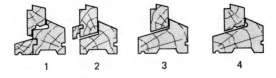

Figure 214 *Self-assessment question*

chapter 6

Construction work

After reading this chapter you should be able to:

1 State the stages involved in site carpentry work.

2 Prepare sketches to show various items of construction work.

3 State the principles involved in various items of construction work.

4 Identify the component parts of various items of construction work.

5 List any building regulations which are relevant to a given item of construction work.

6 Select the most suitable method of construction for a given situation.

Classification of site carpentry

The carpenter's work on site is divided into various stages. These are:

Carcassing   Finishing
First fixing   Temporary and site work
Second fixing

Table 5 shows the work involved in these stages.

Ground floors

Ground floors can be divided into two types:

Suspended timber ground floors (often termed hollow ground floors)
Solid ground floors

Hollow ground floors are the more expensive type of construction. Most houses built pre-1945 have this type of floor. The majority of modern houses have a solid ground floor. The main exception to this would be modern houses that are built on sloping sites. These are normally constructed with a hollow ground floor.

The function of ground floors
The main functions of both types of ground floor are the same:

To provide a suitable floor surface which is both durable and acceptable.

Stage	Work involved
Carcassing	Fixing floor joists. Fixing flat and pitched roof members
First fixing	Laying flooring. Fixing studwork. Fixing door frames and linings. Fixing grounds. Fixing window boards and any other work to be carried out before the building is plastered
Second fixing	Hanging doors. Fitting locks. Fixing skirtings and architraves. Fixing shelves. Pipe casings. Fixing joinery units and any other work to be carried out before the building is decorated
Finishing	Fixing of ironmongery and any other work required to complete the building
Temporary and site work	Erection of centres, formwork, hoardings, fences and site accommodation

Table 5

To carry any loads which may be imposed upon it.

To prevent moisture penetration through the floor.

To provide a certain standard of thermal insulation.

To prevent growth of weeds, etc. inside the building.

Hollow ground floors

Hollow ground floors are made up as shown in Figure 215. The fixing of ground floor joists is normally the first job the carpenter will have to do on site. The joists are cut to length and tosh nailed to the wall plates, which have previously been bedded and levelled on top of the honeycomb sleeper walls by the bricklayer. The size, spacing and support of ground floor joists are governed by the Building Regulations, Schedule 6, Table 1. A common layout is 50 × 100 mm joists spaced 400 mm apart supported at 1.8 m intervals by honeycomb sleeper walls. Air bricks and honeycomb sleeper walls are incorporated into the structure to provide through ventilation to the underfloor space.

The Building Regulations

The Building Regulations lay down certain minimum standards for the construction of hollow ground floors. See Figure 216 (refer to the Building Regulations, Part C):

1 The site of the building must be completely cleared of turf and any other vegetable matter (C2)
2 The floor must be constructed to prevent moisture penetration through the floor (C3)
3 The following minimum requirements for hollow ground floors are deemed to satisfy regulation C3:
   (a) Oversite concrete (1:3:6 mix) at least 100 mm thick, laid on a bed of clean clinker, broken brick or other suitable material which does not contain any harmful substances.
   (b) The surface of the concrete is spade or trowel finished so that its top surface is not below the highest ground or paving level adjoining the building.
   (c) The space between:
      (i) The concrete and the wall plate must be at least 75 mm.
      (ii) The concrete and the underside of the joist must be at least 125 mm. This space must be well ventilated and clear of any debris.
   (d) Damp proof courses (DPC) must be used to ensure the timber cannot be affected by moisture from the ground.

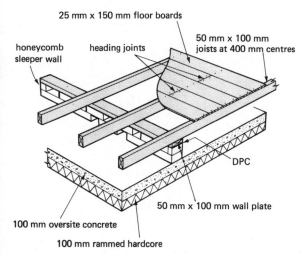

25 mm x 150 mm floor boards

honeycomb sleeper wall

heading joints

50 mm x 100 mm joists at 400 mm centres

DPC

50 mm x 100 mm wall plate

100 mm oversite concrete

100 mm rammed hardcore

Figure 215 *Making up hollow ground floors*

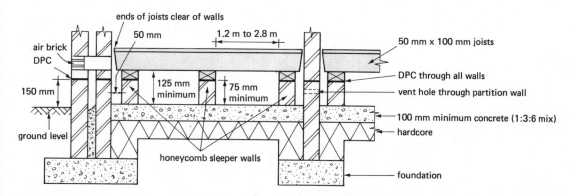

ends of joists clear of walls

air brick
DPC

50 mm

1.2 m to 2.8 m

50 mm x 100 mm joists

125 mm minimum

75 mm minimum

DPC through all walls

vent hole through partition wall

150 mm

100 mm minimum concrete (1:3:6 mix)

hardcore

ground level

honeycomb sleeper walls

foundation

Figure 216 *Building Regulations minimum standards*

Fireplace openings

The use of timber around fireplace openings is controlled by the Building Regulations, Part L. These state that no timber may be built into a flue or nearer than 500 mm from the front, or 150 mm from the side of the fireplace opening. See Figures 217 and 218.

Layout of joists around fireplace

The ends of the joists in front of the fireplace are supported by a wall plate on the fender wall. The fire hearth is framed out with lengths of joist which sit on the fender wall. This framing performs two functions:

It acts as formwork when the fire hearth is concreted.
It supports the ends of the floor boards around the hearth.

Floor boards

Flooring usually consists of 25 × 150 mm softwood boards, tongued and grooved together (T & G), although flooring-grade chipboard is becoming increasingly popular because of its saving in material and labour costs. Figure 219 shows the two methods which are used to fix softwood flooring.

Note: Secret fixing is normally only used on high-class work or hardwood flooring as this method is more expensive because of the increased laying time.

Shown in Figure 220 are two types of heading joint which are used for softwood flooring.

Note: Heading joints should be staggered and not placed next to each other.

Laying floor boards can begin when the roof has been covered. The first board is fixed in front of the hearth or, when no fireplace is present, the board is fixed 10 mm away from the wall. The remainder of the boards are laid four to six at a time. These are cramped up tight with special floor board cramps and then nailed to the joists. Where secret nailing is required, boards must be laid and fixed individually. In order to utilize offcuts of board and avoid wastage, heading joints are introduced as required.

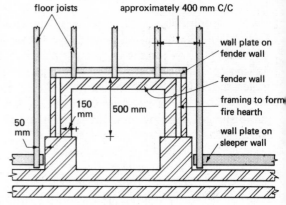

Figure 217   *Use of timber around a fireplace*

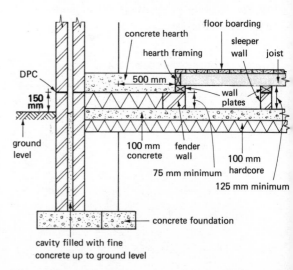

Figure 218   *Typical section through suspended ground floor with fire hearth*

Access to services

When services run under ground floors access is sometimes required at various points, e.g. water stopcock or electric junction box. The best method of providing these access points is shown in Figure 221.

Prevention of decay

Timber ground floors are prone to attack by dry rot fungus. This fungus is dealt with fully in Chapter 3. The main causes of dry rot are:

Damp timber
Bad ventilation

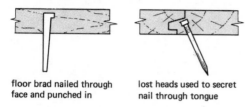

floor brad nailed through face and punched in

lost heads used to secret nail through tongue

Figure 219 *Fixing softwood flooring*

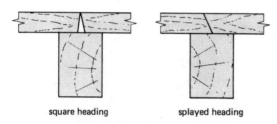

square heading

splayed heading

Figure 220 *Heading joints for softwood flooring*

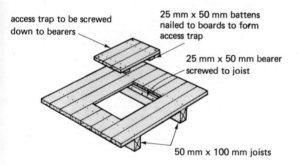

access trap to be screwed down to bearers

25 mm x 50 mm battens nailed to boards to form access trap

25 mm x 50 mm bearer screwed to joist

50 mm x 100 mm joists

Figure 221 *Providing access to services*

The problem of possible attack by dry rot in suspended ground floors is overcome by:

The provision of a damp proof course placed 150 mm above ground level and below all wall plates. This DPC must extend through all internal and external walls.

The provision of adequate ventilation. Through ventilation is provided by air bricks and the honeycombing of the sleeper walls. Air bricks should be placed on opposite walls in order to give a free passage to air under the floor.

Ensuring that no floor timbers come into contact with the external walls.

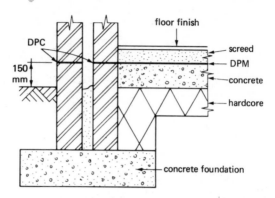

floor finish

DPC

150 mm

screed

DPM

concrete

hardcore

concrete foundation

Figure 222 *Typical solid ground floor construction*

Ensuring that the under floor space is kept clean. This should be cleaned out before the laying of the floor boards.

Solid ground floors

Solid ground floors are made up of:

Floor finish
Screed
Damp proof membrane (DPM)
Concrete
Hardcore

This is shown in Figure 222.

The type of solid floor which the carpenter and joiner is concerned with are those which use timber as the floor finish.

Floor boarding

Hardwood is mainly used for boarding solid ground floors. Different types of heading joints are used on hardwood from those used on softwood boarding. The tongues and grooves are of a special shape to allow for secret nailing.

Timber finish to solid ground floors

There are two main methods which can be used to provide a timber finish to solid ground floors:

1   By using timber bearers which provide a means of fixing for the floor boards. It is most important that a DPM is incorporated in the construction to avoid the timber becoming damp. See Figures 223 and 224.

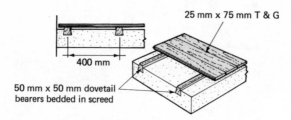

Figure 223   *Timber finish to solid ground floor*

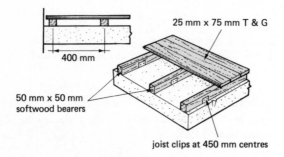

Figure 224   *Timber finish to solid ground floor*

2 By laying flooring directly on to concrete screed. The flooring is fixed by bedding in a bituminous-mastic compound, which also acts as a DPM. This method is mostly used for small parquet blocks.

Roofs

Timber roofs are classified according to their shape. The most common type are:

The flat roof
The lean-to roof
The gable-end roof
The hipped-end roof

See Figure 225.

They may be constructed as either single or double roofs, according to their span.

Single roofs. The rafters of single roofs do not require any intermediate support. See Figure 226.

Double roofs. The rafters of double roofs are of such a length that they require an intermediate support. This support is normally given by purlins. See Figure 227.

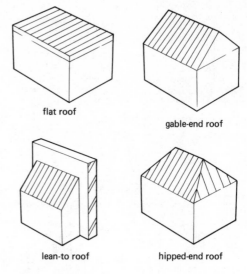

Figure 225   *Types of roof*

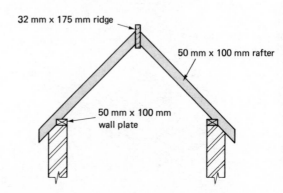

Figure 226   *Section through a single roof*

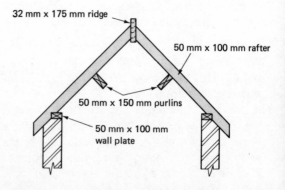

Figure 227   *Section through a double roof*

Roof pitch

The roof pitch is the slope of the roof's surface. This can be expressed in two ways.
In degrees
As rise divided by span

See Figure 228.

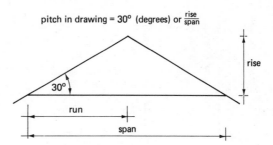

Figure 228   *Roof pitch*

Roof covering

The type of roof covering is governed by the pitch of the roof. In general, as the pitch lowers, the unit size of the covering material must increase.

Table 6 gives the minimum pitches for a range of roof coverings.

Minimum slopes for pitched roof coverings

Material	Slope
	(degrees)
Corrugated materials (protected metal and asbestos)	12
Very large slates (300 mm and 350 mm wide)	25
Large slates (225 mm and 250 mm wide)	30
Single lap tiles (interlocking)	30
Wood shingles (with 125 mm gauge)	30
Stone slates	33
Asbestos cement slates (with 75 mm lap)	35
Medium slates (200 mm wide)	35
Pan tiles	35
Plain tiles	40
Thatch	45
Small slates (150 mm wide)	45

Table 6

Roof terminology (Figure 229)

Rafters

These are the main load-bearing timbers in the roof. They span from wall plate to ridge board. For sizes and spacing of rafters refer to the Building Regulations Schedule 6.

Ridge

This is the backbone of the roof which provides a fixing point for the tops of the rafters. The size of the ridge board is governed by the pitch of the

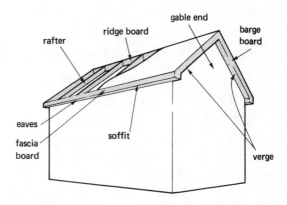

Figure 229   *Roof terminology*

roof. The steeper the pitch the wider the ridge board must be.

Wall plates

These transfer the loads imposed on the roof, uniformly over the supporting brickwork. They also provide a bearing and fixing point for the foot of the rafters.

Eaves

These are the lower ends of the rafters where they overhang the wall.

Fascia board

This is the horizontal board which is fixed to the ends of the rafters. It provides a finish to the eaves and a fixing for the guttering.

Soffit

This is the boarding used to close the gap between the fascia board and the wall.

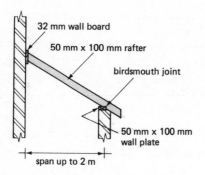

Figure 230   *Lean-to roof*

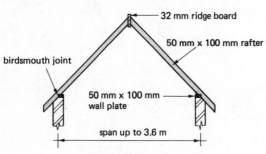

Figure 231   *Couple roof*

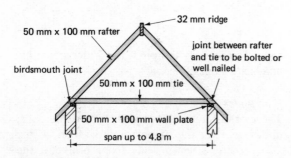

Figure 232   *Close couple roof*

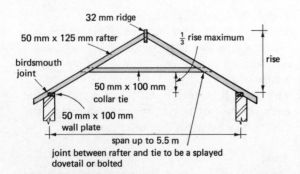

Figure 233   *Collar tie roof*

Verge
This is the sloping edge of the roof where it over-hangs the gable wall.

Gable
This is the triangular section of brickwork at the end of a pitched roof.

Barge board
This is the continuation of the fascia board around the verge.

Types of single roofs
Single roofs only are dealt with in this chapter. Double roofs are covered in *Carpentry and Joinery for Building Craft Students 2*.

The type of single roof used is dependent upon the span of the roof. The four main types are:

Lean-to roof (Figure 230)
Couple roof (Figure 231)
Close couple roof (Figure 232)
Collar tie roof (Figure 233)

Lean-to roofs
These are mono-pitched roofs (only one sloping surface). They are mainly used for roofs to small single storey extensions.

Couple roofs
These have pairs of rafters fixed at one end to the wall plates and at the other to the ridge board. The span is restricted as, without a tie to the feet, the forces which act on the roof have a tendency to spread the walls.

Close couple roofs
These are similar to the couple roofs, but with the feet of the rafters closed with a tie. This enables the span to be increased. The tie also acts as the ceiling joists.

Collar tie roofs
These are similar to the close couple roofs, but in order to increase the span the tie is moved up the rafter a maximum of one third of the rise.

Joints used for pitched roofs

The main types of joint used for pitched roofs are described below.

Birdsmouth joint

This joint is used between the rafters and the wall plate. The birdsmouth is a combination of a plumb and a seat cut, which is taken out one-third the depth of the rafter. The joint is fastened by tosh nailing with 100 mm wire nails. See Figure 234.

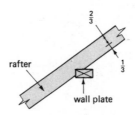

Figure 234   *Birdsmouth joint*

Butt joint

This joint is used between the rafters and the ridge board. The angle of the joint is a plumb cut. It is fastened with 75 mm or 100 mm wire nails. See Figure 235.

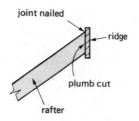

Figure 235   *Butt joint*

Scarf or half-lapped joint

This joint is used to lengthen wall plates. It is fastened with either 50 mm wire nails or preferably screws. See Figure 236.

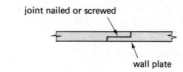

Figure 236   *Half-lapped joint*

Splayed scarf joint

This joint is used to lengthen the ridge board. The proportions of the joint are shown. It is tightened by the use of folding wedges. See Figure 237.

Splayed dovetail joint

This joint is used between the rafters and the collar tie. It is best fastened by the use of a bolt and timber connector, but it is often fastened with wire nails. See Figure 238.

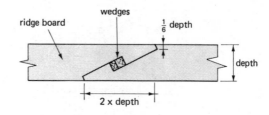

Figure 237   *Splayed scarf joint*

Eaves details

There are three methods of finishing eaves in common use. They are as follows:

Flush eaves (Figure 239)
Open eaves (Figure 240)
Closed eaves (Figure 241)

All three eaves details have one thing in common. This is the sprocket piece. Its purpose is to reduce the pitch of the roof at the eaves. This slows down the flow of rain water off the roof and reduces the tendency for it to overshoot the gutter. The use of sprocket pieces also adds to the appearance of the roof.

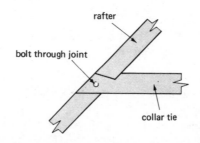

Figure 238   *Splayed dovetail joint*

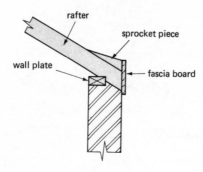

Figure 239   *Flush eaves*

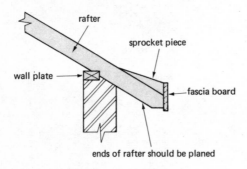

Figure 240   *Open eaves*

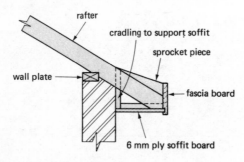

Figure 241   *Closed eaves*

Setting out rafters

There are three main methods used to set out rafters for pitched roofs.

Full-size method

Scale-drawing method (this is dealt with in Chapter 7)

Roofing-square method (this is dealt with in *Carpentry and Joinery for Building Craft Students 2*)

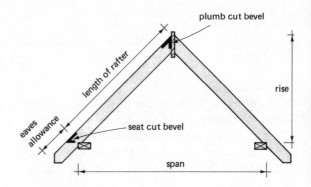

Figure 242   *Full-size setting out*

Full-size method (Figure 242)

This method involves setting out in full size on a suitable surface. The pattern rafter can then be laid on top of this and marked out. The rest of the rafters can then be marked out and cut from the pattern.

Skirting and architraves

Skirting

A skirting is a horizontal timber board which is fixed around the base of a wall. Its function is to protect the plaster from knocks and to cover the joint between the wall and floor.

Skirtings can be fixed in a number of ways.

To timber grounds (Figure 243)

Skirting over 100 mm in depth will require two horizontal grounds and those which are less than 100 mm will only require one horizontal ground. The top of the ground should be approximately 10 mm below the top edge of the skirting. Packing pieces may be needed behind the grounds to provide a true surface on which to fix the skirting.

To timber plugs (Figure 244)

Timber plugs are shaped as shown and driven into the raked-out vertical brickwork joints. The plugs should be placed at approximately 600 mm distances. When all the plugs have been fixed, they should be cut off to provide a true line. An allowance should be made for the thickness of the plaster.

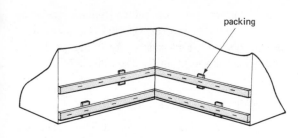

Figure 243 *Fixing skirting to timber grounds*

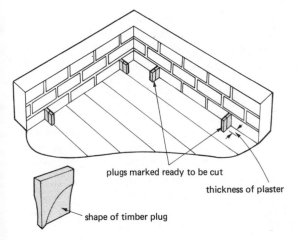

plugs marked ready to be cut

thickness of plaster

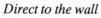

shape of timber plug

Figure 244 *Fixing skirting to timber plugs*

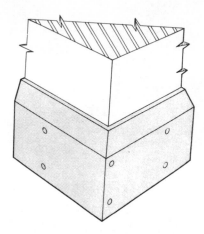

Figure 245 *Mitring external corners*

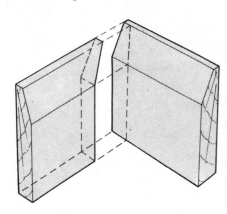

Figure 246 *Scribing internal corners*

Direct to the wall

This is done by using either cut nails or masonry nails depending on the hardness of the wall.

External corners

The external corners of skirting should be mitred as shown in Figure 245. These mitres are cut in a suitable mitre box.

Internal corners

Internal corners are scribed, one piece being cut to fit over the other. See Figure 246. This can be done in two ways:

By cutting an internal mitre on one piece and cutting away the waste.

By scribing with a compass and cutting on the scribed line.

When the floor is uneven, the skirting should be scribed to the floor

The skirting can be kept tight to the floor when nailing by kneeling on a short piece of board.

Architraves

Architraves are the moulded pieces of timber which are fixed around a door opening.

The purpose of architraves is to cover the joint between the frame or lining and the wall.

A set of architraves consists of a head and two jambs. The head is normally fixed first. The mitre joints which are used at the corners of the architrave should be nailed through the top edge. See Figure 247. The normal method of fixing architraves is shown in Figure 248. The nails should be placed in the quirks and punched in.

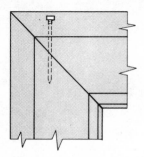

Figure 247   *Nailing mitre joints at corners of architraves*

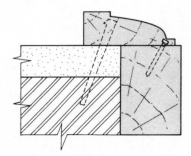

Figure 248   *Normal method of fixing architraves*

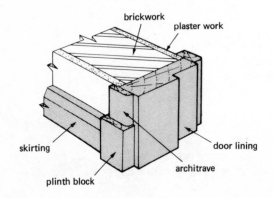

Figure 249   *Use of plinth blocks*

Note: Architraves are fixed to the frame or lining using oval nails and to the wall using cut or masonry nails, depending on the hardness of the wall.

Plinth blocks
Plinth blocks were traditionally used to take the knocks and abrasions at floor level which large moulded section architraves are prone to.

In modern practice plinth blocks are only normally used when the skirting is thicker than the architrave. This eases any fixing problems and provides a neat finish. See Figure 249.

Shelving

The purpose of shelving is to provide a storage space for a particular purpose, depending on the location of the shelving. The type of shelf and shelf support to be used are dependent on two things:

The weight of the items to be stored on the shelf.
The location of the shelf. Shelves for display, in general have an aesthetic quality, whereas shelves for storage tend to be more practical.

Classification of shelves
There are two types of shelves, described below.
   Slatted shelves are mainly used for airing cupboards, etc. to allow a free circulation of warm air. They are also used for wide shelving in order to save timber. See Figure 250.

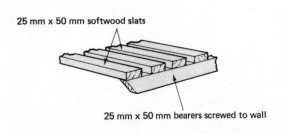

Figure 250   *Slatted shelves*

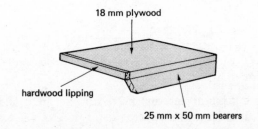

Figure 251   *Solid shelves*

Solid shelves. A wide range of materials can be used according to needs, e.g. glass, steel, wide timber boards, T & G boards, chipboard, blockboard and plywood. When the latter three are used, some form of lipping should be used. See Figures 251 and 252.

Shelf supports

In general there are three ways in which a shelf can be supported.

On bearers

These bearers are 25 × 50 mm softwood which is plugged and screwed to the brickwork along the back and ends of the shelf. See Figures 250 and 251.

On brackets

The main types being:

Gallows brackets (for heavy loads) (Figure 252)
Mild steel brackets (for medium loads)
Cantilever brackets (for light loads) (Figure 253)

On a combination of bearers and brackets

This is a method used mainly for higher quality work. See Figure 254.

Temporary work

There are two items of temporary work covered in this chapter.

Centres for arches
Formwork for concrete

Centres for arches

To enable a bricklayer to build an arch, he requires a centre to be made by the carpenter. The centre acts as a temporary support to the brickwork. There are two main types of centre.

A turning piece. This is a solid piece of timber cut to the shape of a flat or segmental arch. It is only suitable for arches in half brick walls (103 mm) which are of low rise, up to 150 mm from the springing line. See Figure 255.

Built-up centres. These are used where the rise exceeds 150 mm and one brick or more in depth. Centres for low rises up to 200 mm have solid

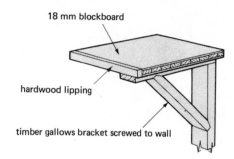

Figure 252 *Gallows brackets*

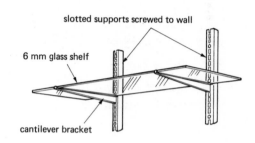

Figure 253 *Cantilever brackets*

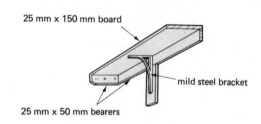

Figure 254 *Use of a combination of bearers and brackets*

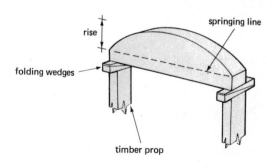

Figure 255 *Turning piece*

ribs. See Figure 256. For rises in excess of this, made-up or laminated ribs must be used. Figure 257 shows a built-up centre with laminated ribs which is suitable for rises up to 500 mm and a span of 1 m. Where the width of the brickwork exceeds half a brick, cross braces should be used to stiffen the centre. The two sets of ribs are spanned by lagging which should be 20 mm shorter than the depth of the arch. This ensures that the centre will not obstruct the bricklayer in levelling and plumbing the brickwork. Timber battens or plywood may be used for the lagging depending on the type of work in hand. In general, close timber lagging or plywood is used for brickwork and open laggings are used for stonework. See Figure 257.

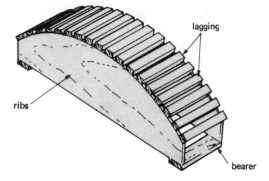

Figure 256   *Built-up centre*

Support of centres

Centres are supported, levelled and adjusted by means of either:

Adjustable props
Timber posts and folding wedges

The use of the props or wedges also facilitates the easing and striking (removal) of the centre without damage to the finished brickwork.

Figure 258 shows the inner ribs, outer ribs, struts and tie, nailed together with their joints staggered. These nails should be clenched over.

Note: The outline of the arch is marked on and the centre is ready to be cut on the band saw, or if the centre is being made on site it would be cut with a portable power jig saw.

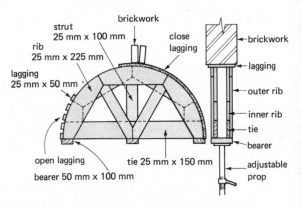

Figure 257   *Built-up centre with laminated ribs*

Setting out

Small semicircular arches can be set out with a radius rod (see Figure 259), but for larger centres and segmental curves a triangular template is normally used. See Figure 260. The frame is moved around the curve on the two nails. The marking is done with a pencil as shown. When marking the curve an allowance must be made for the thickness of the laggings.

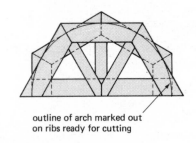

outline of arch marked out
on ribs ready for cutting

Figure 258   *Marking out ribs*

Formwork for concrete

Formwork is a temporary structure which is designed to shape and support wet concrete until

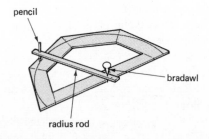

Figure 259   *Semicircular arch set out with radius rod*

it cures sufficiently to become self-supporting. When designing formwork the following features should be borne in mind:

Strength of materials used for the formwork
Economical use of materials
Ease of making and erecting formwork
Facilities for adjustment, levelling, easing and striking of the formwork
The quality of finish required

Planed European redwood is mainly used for formwork, although it is now common practice on many sites to use Douglas fir plywood for the surfaces of formwork in contact with the concrete. The use of plywood produces a better finish and also shortens the time taken to erect the formwork. When a high-quality finish to the concrete is required the formwork can be lined with exterior grade plywood, hardboard or plastic laminate. Before concreting, the formwork should be coated with a mould oil, in order to prevent the concrete adhering to the timber.

When formwork has been struck, it should be cleaned, de-nailed, repaired and stored ready for re-use. Metal props and bolts should be cleaned, coated with a rust inhibitor and have their threads lubricated with oil.

Types of casting

There are two ways in which concrete products can be manufactured:

Pre-cast
Cast *in situ*

Pre-cast concrete. In this method the product is cast in a factory, or out of location on site. It is later placed in its final location, e.g. lintels, paving slabs, blocks, etc.

Concrete cast in situ. In this method, as its name suggests, the concrete is cast in the actual location where it is required, e.g. larger lintels or beams, drives and bases.

Figure 261 shows details of a pre-cast formwork mould for lintels.

Note: Before assembling the moulds, the carpenter must ensure that the bases are level and out of wind. If this is not done, the finished concrete items would be distorted.

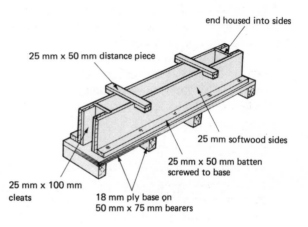

Figure 261   *Formwork for pre-cast lintel*

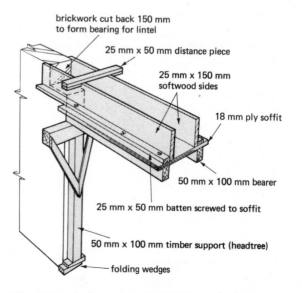

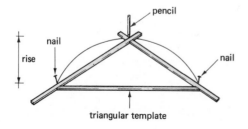

Figure 260   *Use of a triangular template*

Figure 262   *Formwork for* in situ *lintel*

Figure 262 shows details of the formwork required for an *in situ* lintel up to 1.2 m in length.

The formwork is levelled by means of the folding wedges under the timber supports. An alternative means of support and levelling, now used on most sites, is the adjustable steel prop.

Note: The brickwork is cut back at both ends to form a bearing for the lintel.

Distance pieces should be used at approximately 450 mm distances in order to stop the formwork bulging under the pressure of the concrete.

When formwork is required for a small concrete base, e.g. garden shed, coal store, patio, etc., timber or ply sides can be levelled and fixed to 50 × 50 mm pointed pegs, which are spaced at approximately 1 m. Care must be taken to ensure that the base is square. This is done by measuring the diagonals. When the diagonals are equal the base is square.

Self-assessment questions

1   The component that links the tops of the rafters is a
    (a) wall plate
    (b) collar tie
    (c) purlin
    (d) ridge board

2   A semicircular centre is used to support a brick arch during its construction. The actual part of the centre which is in contact with the brickwork is the
    (a) bearers
    (b) lagging
    (c) ribs
    (d) braces

3   The joint used at the intersection of the rafter and wall plate is
    (a) birdsmouth
    (b) splayed dovetail
    (c) half-lapped joint
    (d) butt joint

4   The purpose of using mould oil on formwork is
    (a) to help the concrete set
    (b) to clean the formwork
    (c) to stop the concrete adhering to the formwork
    (d) to stop the formwork rotting

5   The minimum height of a sleeper wall in a suspended timber ground floor is
    (a) 75 mm
    (b) 125 mm
    (c) 150 mm
    (d) 100 mm

6   The most suitable type of shelf for use in an airing cupboard would be
    (a) blockboard
    (b) T & G boarding
    (c) timber slats
    (d) solid boarding

7   The roof section shown in Figure 263 is of a
    (a) couple roof
    (b) close-couple roof
    (c) trussed rafter
    (d) collar tie roof

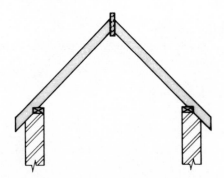

Figure 263   *Self-assessment question*

8   The levelling, easing and striking of formwork for an *in situ* concrete lintel can be carried out by means of
    (a) fox wedges
    (b) adjustable beam cramp
    (c) folding wedges
    (d) timber prop

9 The angle of intersection between the common rafter and the ridge board is known as the
   (a) seat cut
   (b) ridge cut
   (c) plumb cut
   (d) purlin cut

10 Architraves are fixed around a door opening to
   (a) provide a fixing for the door stop
   (b) cover joint between frame or lining and wall
   (c) fix frame or lining to wall
   (d) give a straight line for the plasterer to work to

chapter 7

Basic drawing practice and geometry

After reading this chapter you should be able to:

1 List a number of recommendations given in BS 1192.

2 Recognize symbols and abbreviations given in BS 1192.

3 Identify the main types of projection which are used in building drawing.

4 Prepare simple scale drawings.

5 Prepare drawings to show various geometrical constructions involving lines, angles, triangles, quadrilaterals and circles.

6 Prepare drawings to show the basic geometrical constructions involved in roofing.

Drawing

The main method used to communicate technical information in the building industry is by the use of drawings.

The student will find that much of his carpentry and joinery technology will consist of drawing and geometry. It is therefore essential that a student develops his ability to produce and understand a wide range of drawings and sketches.

All building drawings should be produced in accordance with BS 1192, 1969 'Building Drawing Practice'. By doing this it ensures that all building drawings are standardized and are therefore fully understood by everyone who uses them.

Working drawings

These are scale drawings showing the plans, elevations, sections, details and locality of a proposed construction. These drawings can be classified into three types.

Location drawings

Block plans. These identify the proposed site in relation to the surrounding area.

Site plans. These give the position of the proposed building and the general layout of roads, services and drainage, etc. on the site.

General location plans. These show the position occupied by the various areas within the building and identify the location of the principle elements and components.

Component drawings

Range drawings. These show the basic sizes and reference system of a standard range of components.

Detail drawings. These show all the information that is required in order to manufacture a given component.

Assembly drawings

These show in detail the junctions in and between the various elements and components of a building.

Types of line

Shown in Figure 264 are the various types of lines which are used in building drawing and geometry. The use of these lines are given in Table 7.

Dimensions

Figure 265 shows the correct sequence of dimensioning. Where dimensions are listed on a drawing, the length should be given first followed by the width and then, thirdly, the height or depth. Where only two dimensions are used, they should be listed in the same order. It must be

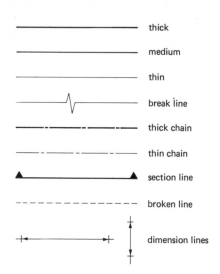

Figure 264   *Types of line*

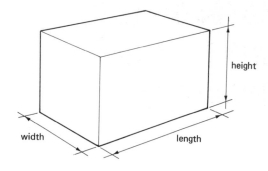

Figure 265   *Correct sequence of dimensioning*

Type	Used for
1 Thick	Main outlines
2 Medium	General details and outlines
3 Thin	Construction and dimension lines
4 Breakline	Breaks in the continuity of a drawing
5 Thick chain	Pipe lines, drains and services
6 Thin chain	Centre lines
7 Section line	Showing the position of a cut (the pointers indicate the direction of view)
8 Broken line	Showing details which are not visible
9 Dimension line	Showing the distance between two points

Table 7

noted however that throughout this book in line with common practice in the timber industry, the sizes of pieces of timber have been given in the following sequence:

1 Thickness (the smallest dimension of the section)
2 Width (the largest dimension of the section)

PRINTING FOR TITLES SHOULD BE 7mm HIGH

3mm HIGH PRINTING SHOULD BE USED FOR NOTES AND ANY OTHER INFORMATION WHICH IS REQUIRED ON A DRAWING SHEET

FREEHAND PRINTING SHOULD BE BETWEEN TWO FAINT CONSTRUCTION LINES

TWO PARALLEL LINES 3mm APART

Figure 266   *Sizes of printing*

Printing
The recommended sizes for letters and numbers on drawings is between 5 mm and 8 mm for titles and between 1.5 mm and 4 mm for notes. An example of printing is given in Figure 266. It shows the sizes of printing the student will normally use.

Note: All printing on drawings should be placed between two faint construction lines.

Layout of drawing sheet
Before starting on the actual drawing, the drawing sheet should be laid out as shown in Figure 267.

Note: The title panel printing should be 7 mm high.

Figure 268 shows a typical drawing sheet information panel, used by many drawing offices.

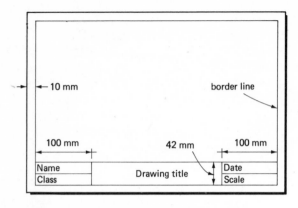

Figure 267   *Layout of drawing sheet*

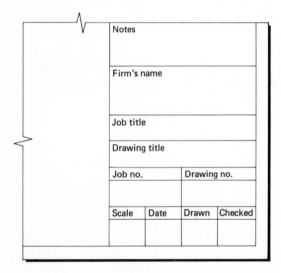

Figure 268   *Typical drawing sheet information panel*

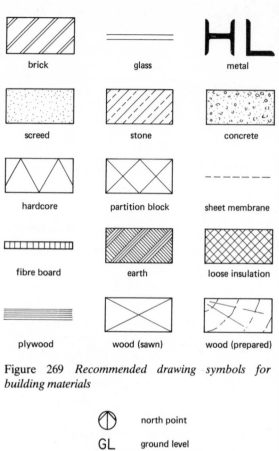

Figure 269   *Recommended drawing symbols for building materials*

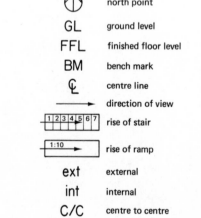

Figure 270   *Frequently used graphical symbols (BS 1192)*

Symbols and abbreviations

The use of symbols and abbreviations in building drawings enables the maximum amount of information to be included on a drawing sheet in a clear and concise way.

Figure 269 shows the recommended drawing symbols for a number of building materials.

Figure 270 illustrates some of the most frequently used graphical symbols which are recommended in BS 1192.

Figure 271 shows the recommended method of indicating the type and direction of opening of doors and windows.

There are a large number of standard abbreviations, which are recommended for use in building drawing. The following is a list of the main abbreviations that a carpentry and joinery student will be concerned with.

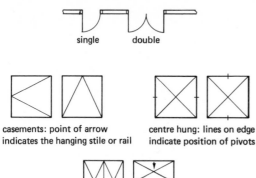

casements: point of arrow
indicates the hanging stile or rail

centre hung: lines on edge
indicate position of pivots

sliding: arrows indicate direction of opening

Figure 271   *Direction of opening doors and windows*

Airbrick	AB	Hardwood	hwd
Asbestos	abs	Insulation	insul
Bitumen	bit	Joist	jst
Boarding	bdg	Mild steel	MS
Brickwork	bwk	Plasterboard	pbd
Building	bldg	Polyvinyl	
Cast iron	CI	acetate	PVA
Cement	ct	Polyvinyl	
Column	col	chloride	PVC
Concrete	conc	Reinforced	
Cupboard	cpd	concrete	RC
Damp proof		Satin chrome	SC
course	DPC	Satin anodised	
Damp proof		aluminium	SAA
membrane	DPM	Softwood	swd
Drawing	dwg	Stainless steel	SS
Foundation	fdn	Tongue and	
Hardcore	hc	groove	T & G
Hardboard	hdb	Wrought iron	WI

Types of projection

There are many methods by which a particular object can be drawn, each method giving a different view of that object. The four main methods which the carpentry and joinery student will come across are:

Orthographic
Isometric
Oblique
Axonometric

Orthographic

Orthographic projection is the method most commonly used in the building industry for detailed construction drawings. This method entails producing a separate drawing of all the views of an object in a systematic manner on the same drawing sheet. There are two internationally recognized methods of laying out the various views on the drawing sheet. These are:

First angle projection. (This is also called European projection.)
Third angle projection. (This is also called American projection.)

In Britain first angle projection is recommended for building drawings, while third angle projection is recommended for engineering drawings.

Figure 272 identifies the views for orthographic projection.

View A is the view from the front.
View B is the view from above.
View C is the view from the left.
View D is the view from the right.
View E is the view from below.
View F is the view from the rear.

The difference between first and third angle projection is the layout of the views. This is shown in Figures 273 and 274. In both methods the view from the front is the first to be drawn.

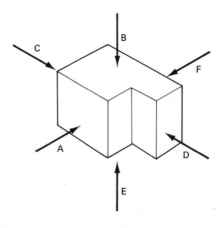

Figure 272   *Views for orthographic projection*

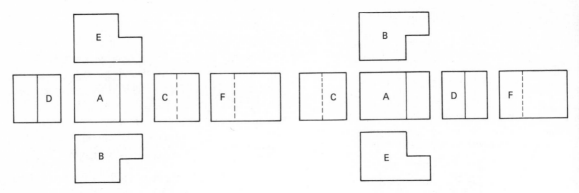

Figure 273   *First angle projection*   Figure 274   *Third angle projection*

First angle projection
In relation to the front view the other views are arranged as follows:

The view from above is drawn below.
The view from below is drawn above.
The view from the left is drawn to the right.
The view from the right is drawn to the left.
The view from the rear is drawn on the extreme right.

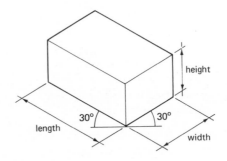

Figure 275   *Isometric projection*

Third angle projection
In relation to the front view the other views are arranged as follows:

The view from above is drawn above.
The view from below is drawn below.
The view from the left is drawn to the left.
The view from the right is drawn to the right.
The view from the rear is drawn on the extreme right.

Note: Broken lines indicate hidden detail.

Pictorial projection
Isometric, oblique and axonometric are all pictorial methods of projection. These are often used for design and marketing purposes, as the finished appearance of an object can be more readily appreciated from a pictorial projection, rather than from an orthographic projection.

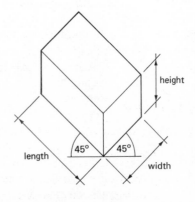

Figure 276   *Axonometric projection*

Isometric projection (Figure 275)
All vertical lines are drawn vertical, while horizontal lines are drawn at 30 degrees to the horizontal.

Axonometric projection (Figure 276)
This is similar to isometric projection, the difference being that the horizontal lines are drawn at 45 degrees to the horizontal.

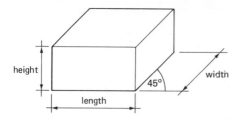

Figure 277 *Cavalier oblique projection*

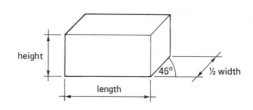

Figure 278 *Cabinet oblique projection*

Oblique projection

There are two types of oblique projection, cavalier (Figure 277) and cabinet (Figure 278).

In both types the lines are constructed as follows:

All vertical lines are drawn vertical.

All horizontal lines in the front view are drawn horizontal. (This gives a true front view.)

All horizontal lines on the side view are drawn at 45 degrees to the horizontal.

In cavalier these 45 degree lines are drawn to their full length, but in cabinet, the 45 degree lines are drawn to half their full length. (This lessens the distorted view which cavalier gives.)

It is up to the student to use his own judgement when deciding the best method of projection to use for a particular drawing. His decision will depend on its purpose.

In Figure 279 a bench hook has been drawn using three of the pictorial methods of projection. Can you identify them?

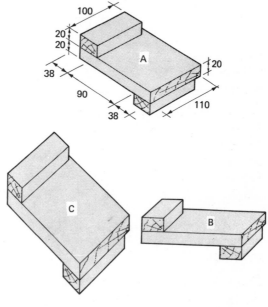

Figure 279 *Three pictorial methods of projection*

Drawing equipment

All students on a carpentry and joinery course at a college will require a set of drawing equipment. It is in the student's own interest to purchase a set of good-quality drawing instruments which will serve him well, in both his course and later in his career.

A minimum set of drawing instruments would consist of:

Set squares   Scale rule
Protractor   Pencils
Compasses   Eraser
Dividers

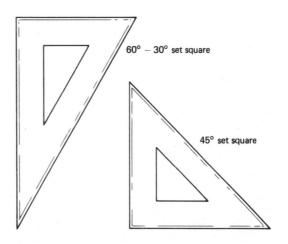

Figure 280 *Set squares*

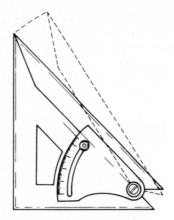

Figure 281   *Adjustable set square*

Figure 282   *Protractor*

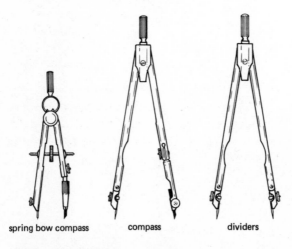

spring bow compass   compass   dividers

Figure 283   *Compasses and dividers*

Set squares (Figure 280)
Two fairly large set squares are required. One a 45 degree square and the other a 60 – 30 degree square. These are used to draw vertical and inclined lines.

An adjustable set square, shown in Figure 281, can be purchased as an alternative. This square can be adjusted to any required angle. It can therefore perform all the functions of the two ordinary set squares and also act as a protractor.

Protractor (Figure 282)
This is used for the setting out and measurement of angles. The most useful sizes have a diameter of between 100 mm and 150 mm.

Note: Set squares, protractors and rules should occasionally be washed in warm, soapy water.

Compasses and dividers (Figure 283)
This shows a set of typical instruments. The large compass is used to draw large circles and arcs, while for accurate, fine work the spring bow compass should be used. Dividers are used for transferring measurements and dividing lines.

Scale rule (Figure 284)
A scale rule which contains the following scales, 1:5/1:50, 1:10/1:100, 1:20/1:200, 1:250/1:2500, is to be recommended.

Pencils (Figure 285)
Two pencils are required, one HB for printing and sketching and either a 2H or 3H for drawing. The pencils should be sharpened as shown, the chisel-shaped edge pencil being used for line work, while the pointed pencil is used for curves and lettering.

Eraser (Figure 286)
A vinyl or rubber eraser is required for alterations or corrections to pencil lines. The eraser

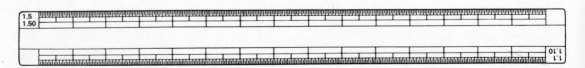

Figure 284   *Scale rule*

must be of a soft type so that the surface of the drawing paper is not damaged while erasing.

Lettering templates (Figure 287)
These are a useful aid for printing titles, etc. on drawings. A wide range of sizes is available.

French curves (Figure 288)
These can be used for drawing complex or irregular curved lines which cannot be easily drawn with compasses.

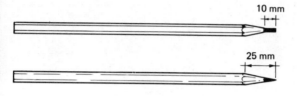

Figure 285   *Pencils*

Figure 286   *Eraser*

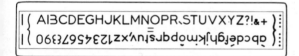

Figure 287   *Lettering template*

Figure 288   *French curve*

Drawing boards and tee squares
Although these are supplied by the college for use while you are there, students should consider either purchasing or making a drawing board and tee square for their use at home.

Scales

In order to draw a building on a drawing sheet, the building must be reduced in size. This is called a scale drawing. The preferred scales for use in building drawing are as follows:

Block plans	1 : 2500
	1 : 1250
Site plans	1 : 500
	1 : 200
General location drawings	1 : 200
	1 : 100
	1 : 50
Range drawings	1 : 100
	1 : 50
	1 : 20
Detail drawings	1 : 10
	1 : 5
	1 : 1
Assembly drawings	1 : 20
	1 : 10
	1 : 5

The use of scales can be easily mastered with a little practice. It must be remembered that a scale is merely a convenient way of reducing a drawing in size.

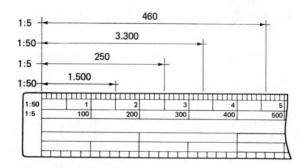

Figure 289   *Scale rule*

1:1 means full size, 10 mm on the drawing represents 10 mm in the building. 1:5 means that 10 mm on the drawing represents 50 mm in the building. 1:50 means that 10 mm on the drawing represents 500 mm in the building.

Figure 289 shows a scale rule with various dimensions indicated above. On the 1:50 scale each small division represents 100 mm whereas on the 1:5 scale each division represents 10 mm.

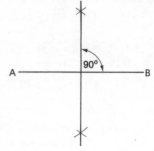

Figure 290   *Bisecting a line*

Lines

There are two simple operations with lines which occur repeatedly in geometry. These are:

Bisecting a line, or dividing it into two equal parts.
Dividing a line into a greater number of equal parts.

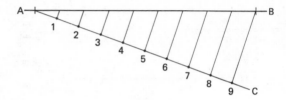

Figure 291   *Dividing a straight line into a given number of equal parts*

Figure 290 shows the method used to bisect a given line:

1 Draw line AB.
2 With centre A and a radius greater than half AB, mark arcs above and below line AB.
3 With centre B and same radius, mark arcs above and below line AB to cross the previous ones.
4 Draw a line through the intersections of the arcs.
Note: This line will bisect the given line at 90 degrees.

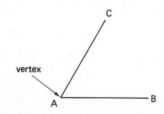

Figure 292   *An angle*

Figure 291 shows a method of dividing a given line into a number of equal parts:

1 Draw given line AB.
2 Draw line AC any length at a convenient angle to line AB.
3 Mark on AC the number of equal parts required. Any convenient spacing is suitable.
4 Join the last numbered point to B.
5 Draw lines through each of the numbered points parallel to the line drawn in stage 4.

The line AB will now be divided into the required number of equal parts.

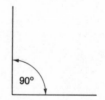

Figure 293   *Right angle*

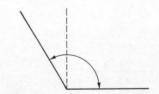

Figure 294   *Obtuse angle*

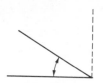

Figure 295 *Acute angle*

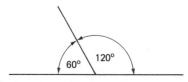

Figure 296 *Supplementary angles*

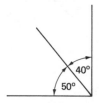

Figure 297 *Complementary angles*

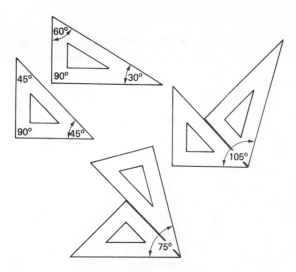

Figure 298 *Angles using set squares*

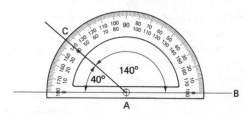

Figure 299 *Angles using a protractor*

Angles

An angle is formed when two inclined lines touch. See Figure 292. The point where the lines touch is called the vertex. A convenient way of referring to angles is by labelling them. The angle shown in Figure 292 can be referred to as BÂC or CÂB. The vertex always being the middle letter.

A *right angle* (Figure 293) is formed where the lines touch at an angle of 90 degrees.

An *obtuse angle* (Figure 294) is an angle greater than 90 degrees.

An *acute angle* (Figure 295) is an angle less than 90 degrees.

Supplementary angles (Figure 296) are two angles which make up 180 degrees. In the example shown 120 degrees is the supplement of 60 degrees and vice versa.

Complementary angles (Figure 297) are two angles which make up 90 degrees. In the example shown, 50 degrees is the complement of 40 degrees and vice versa.

Construction of angles

Angles can be drawn using the following methods:

Using a set square
With a protractor
Using a set of compasses
From a scale of chords

Set squares

A number of different angles can be formed using set squares either separately or combined. Figure 298 shows some of the angles which can be constructed using this method.

The protractor

All angles can be set out or measured using a protractor. Figure 299 shows a protractor being used to set out an angle of 140 degrees:

1 Draw line AB
2 Place protractor over line AB.

Note: Vertex of the angle should always be placed under point ⊕ on the protractor.

3 Mark point C at the required angle.

4 Remove protractor and draw a line between points A and C.

CÂB is the required angle.

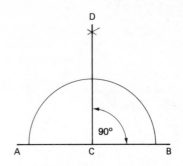

Figure 300   *Forming a right angle with a compass*

Angles using compasses

Almost any angle can be formed using compasses. Figure 300 shows how a right angle is formed. This is a similar method to that used when bisecting a straight line.

In Figure 301 a 45 degree angle is formed by the bisection of a 90 degree angle. The method used is as follows:

1 Construct a right angle as before.

2 With centre A and any convenient radius, draw arc ED.

3 With centre E and a radius of over half ED, mark a small arc over ED.

4 With centre D and same radius as stage 3, mark a small arc to cross the previous one.

5 Draw a line through the intersection of the small arcs and A. This forms two 45 degree angles.

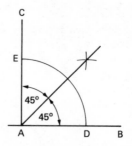

Figure 301   *Forming a 45° angle with a compass*

Figure 302 shows how 30 degree and 60 degree angles can be formed. The procedure is as follows:

1 Construct a right angle as before.

2 With centre A and radius set to AB, draw arc BC.

3 With centre B and radius set to AB, mark point D on arc.

4 With centre C and radius set to AB, mark point E on arc.

5 Draw lines from A to D and A to E.

Angle DÂB will be 60 degrees and angle EÂB will be 30 degrees.

Angles other than 30 degrees, 45 degrees and 60 degrees can be formed by further bisection.

Figure 303 shows an angle of 15 degrees which has been formed by the bisection of a 30 degree angle. The 30 degree angle is bisected using a similar method to that used when forming the 45 degree angle.

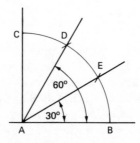

Figure 302   *Forming 30° and 60° angles with a compass*

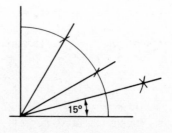

Figure 303   *Forming a 15° angle with a compass*

Scale of chords

Figure 304 shows a scale of chords. The scale is often set out on a strip of plywood and used in the workshop for setting out various angles.

The method used to construct the scale is as follows:

1 Draw line AB.
2 Draw line CD at right angles to AB.
3 With centre D and any convenient radius draw arc BC.
4 Mark on arc BC, 30 degree and 60 degree points. (Use the same method as shown for constructing 30 degree and 60 degree angles.)
5 Divide the three spaces 0 – 30 degrees, 30 – 60 degrees and 60 – 90 degrees on arc BC into three equal parts using dividers.
6 With centre B, draw arcs from all points down on to AB.
7 Construct scale below AB as shown.

Note: By further subdivision of arc BC a wide range of angles can be obtained.

Using a scale of chords

In Figure 305 an angle of 70 degrees has been set out using a scale of chords.

The method used to produce the angle is as follows:

1 Draw line AB.
2 With centre A and radius set from 0 to 60 degrees on the scale, draw arc BC.
3 With centre B and radius set from 0 to 70 degrees on the scale, mark point C on arc BC.
4 Draw line AC. This produces the required angle CÂB.

Note: The radius for the arc BC is always 0 to 60 degrees, no matter what angle is being produced.

Figure 306 shows an angle of 40 degrees which has been set out using a scale of chords. The method used to produce the angle is the same as before, except that in stage 3 the radius must be set from 0 degrees to the required angle.

Triangles

A triangle is a plane figure which is bounded by three straight lines.

Triangles may be classified in two ways:

By the *length of the sides*. Figure 307 shows an equilateral triangle, in which all sides are of equal

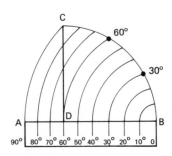

Figure 304   *Scale of chords*

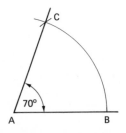

Figure 305   *A 70° angle set out with a scale of chords*

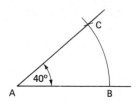

Figure 306   *A 40° angle set out with a scale of chords*

Figure 307   *Equilateral triangle*

Figure 308   *Isosceles triangle*

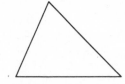

Figure 309   *Scalene triangle*

Figure 310   *Right-angled triangle*

Figure 311   *Acute-angled triangle*

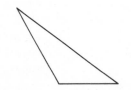

Figure 312   *Obtuse-angled triangle*

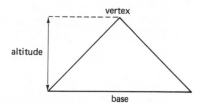

Figure 313   *Terms associated with triangles*

length. Figure 308 shows an isosceles triangle in which any two sides are of equal length. Figure 309 shows a scalene triangle, in which all three sides are unequal in length.

By *the size of the angles*. Figure 310 shows a right-angled triangle in which one angle must measure 90 degrees. Figure 311 shows an acute-angled triangle, in which all of the angles measure less than 90 degrees. Figure 312 shows an obtuse-angled triangle, in which one of the angles measures over 90 degrees and under 180 degrees.

Figure 313 shows the various terms associated with triangles.

1 Vertex. The angle opposite the base.
2 Altitude. The vertical height of the triangle.
3 Perimeter. The length of the three sides.

Note: The longest side of a right-angled triangle is called the hypotenuse.

Construction of triangles

In order to construct a triangle, any one of the following four sets of information is required.

The lengths of the three sides.
The lengths of two sides and the included angle.
The length of one side and two angles.
The length of the perimeter and the ratio of the sides.

The construction of a triangle using these four methods is as follows.

Method 1 (Figure 314)

To construct an equilateral triangle with a base of 100 mm:

1 Draw base AB 100 mm long.
2 From A set radius AB, mark arc BC.
3 From B set radius BA, mark arc AC.
4 Join points AC and BC.

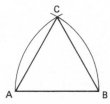

Figure 314   *Constructing a triangle: method 1*

Method 2 (Figure 315)

To construct a triangle with a base of 100 mm, one side of 85 mm and an included angle of 30 degrees:

1 Draw base AB 100 mm long.
2 From A, draw a line at 30 degrees.
3 Mark point C 85 mm from A.
4 Draw line BC.

Method 3 (Figure 316)

To construct a triangle with a base of 100 mm and

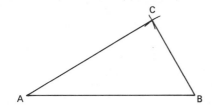

Figure 315   *Constructing a triangle: method 2*

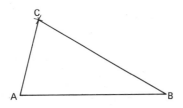

Figure 316   *Constructing a triangle: method 3*

an angle of 75 degrees at one end, and an angle of 30 degrees at the other end:

1   Draw base AB 100 mm long.
2   From A, draw a line at 75 degrees.
3   From B, draw a line at 30 degrees. The lines cross at C.
4   Draw lines AC and BC.

Method 4 (Figure 317)
To construct a triangle which has a perimeter of 200 mm and sides with a ratio of 4:6:5:

1   Draw line AB 200 mm long.
2   Divide AB into 4:6:5 units (as shown).
3   From C with radius set at length CA, mark arc.

4   From D with set radius DB, mark arc. (The arcs cross at E.)
5   Draw lines CE and DE.

Note: The method used to divide line AB is similar to the method used to divide the line shown in Figure 291.

3:4:5 *rule*
Figure 318 illustrates a geometric principle, which is known as Pythagoras' Theorem. According to this theorem, in any right-angled triangle, the square of the hypotenuse is equal to the sum of the square of the other two sides. Therefore, a triangle whose sides are 3 units, 4 units, and 5 units, must be a right-angled triangle, since, $5^2 = 3^2 + 4^2$.

This principle is often used for setting out on site. Figure 319 shows how a right angle can be set out using a tape measure.

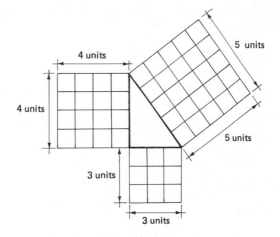

Figure 318   *Pythagoras' Theorem*

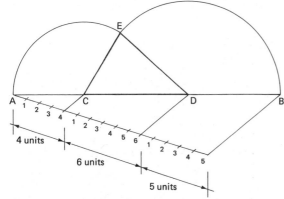

Figure 317   *Constructing a triangle: method 4*

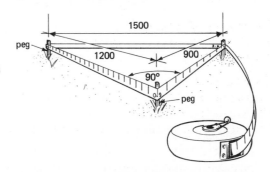

Figure 319   *A 90° angle set out with a tape measure*

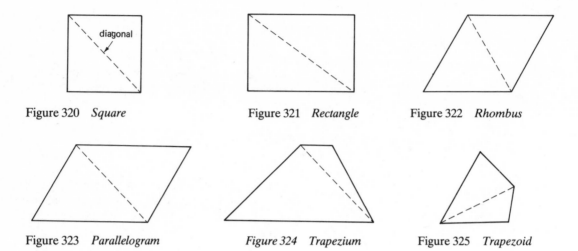

Figure 320   *Square*   Figure 321   *Rectangle*   Figure 322   *Rhombus*

Figure 323   *Parallelogram*   *Figure 324   Trapezium*   Figure 325   *Trapezoid*

Quadrilaterals

A quadrilateral is a plane figure which is bounded by four straight lines. The main types of quadrilaterals are:

A *square* (Figure 320). This has four sides of equal length and four right angles.

A *rectangle* (Figure 321). This has opposite sides of equal length and four right angles.

A *rhombus* (Figure 322). This has four equal sides, opposite sides being parallel, but none of the angles is a right angle.

A *parallelogram* (Figure 323). This has opposite sides which are parallel and equal in length, but none of its angles is a right angle.

Note: A rhombus is a special type of parallelogram where all four sides are equal in length.

A *trapezium* (Figure 324). This has two parallel sides.

A *trapezoid* (Figure 325). This has no parallel sides.

In all quadrilaterals, a straight line joining the opposite angles is called a diagonal. It divides the figure into two triangles.

Squares and rectangles can be constructed using set squares, while the other four quadrilaterals are constructed using a similar method to that used in the construction of triangles.

When constructing quadrilaterals sufficient information is required. This information is:

For a square, the length of the base.

For a rectangle, the lengths of the base and a side.

For a rhombus, the length of the base and one angle.

For a parallelogram, the length of the base, the vertical height and one angle.

For a trapezium, the lengths of the parallel sides, the vertical height and one base angle.

For a trapezoid, the lengths of three sides and the angles between them.

Circles

A circle is a plane figure, bounded by a continuous, curved line, which at every point is an equal distance from the centre.

Figures 326 and 327 show the main elements of a circle:

1   *Circumference.* The curved outer line of the circle.

2   *Diameter.* A straight line which passes through the centre and is terminated at both ends by the circumference.

3   *Radius.* The distance from the centre to the circumference.

   Note: The radius is always half the length of the diameter.

4   *Chord.* A straight line which touches the circumference at two points but does not pass through the centre.

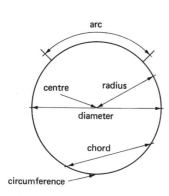
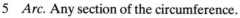

Figure 326   *Elements of a circle*

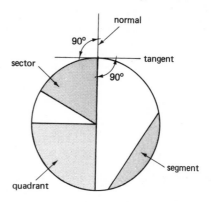

Figure 327   *Elements of a circle*

5   *Arc.* Any section of the circumference.
6   *Normal.* Any straight line which starts at the centre and extends beyond the circumference.
7   *Tangent.* A straight line which touches the circumference at right angles to the normal.
8   *Sector.* The portion of a circle contained between two radii and an arc.
     Note: Radii is the plural of radius.
9   *Quadrant.* A sector whose area is equal to a quarter of the circle.
10   *Segment.* The portion of a circle contained between an arc and a chord.

Concentric circles (Figure 328)
These are circles which share the same centre, but have differing radii.

Eccentric circles (Figure 329)
These are circles drawn within each other from different centres.

Constructions with circles
Figure 330 shows the method used to find the centre of a given circle.

1   Draw on the circle any two chords, AB and CD.
2   Bisect AB and CD.
     The point where the two bisections cross is the required centre.

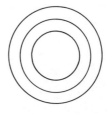

Figure 328   *Concentric circles*

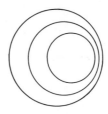

Figure 329   *Eccentric circles*

Figure 331 shows how to construct a segment of a circle. This method can be used when setting out a turning piece or centre for a segmental arch:

1   Draw line AB equal to the span.
2   Bisect AB.
3   From C, mark the rise. Let this point be D.

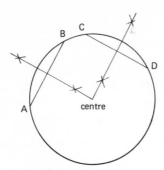

Figure 330   *Finding the centre of a circle*

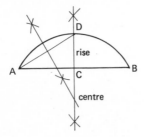

Figure 331   *Constructing a segment of a circle*

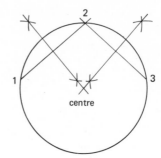

Figure 332   *Drawing a circle to pass through three points*

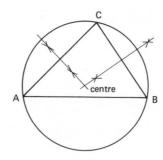

Figure 333   *A triangle circumscribed with a circle*

4   Draw line AD and bisect it. The point where the two bisections cross is the required centre.
5   With radius set from centre to A, the arc can be drawn.

Figure 332 shows how to draw a circle which will pass through any three given points (providing these points are not in a straight line):

1   Connect the three points with straight lines.
2   Bisect the lines. The point where the two bisections cross is the required centre.
3   With radius set from the centre to any one of the points, the circle then can be drawn to pass through all three points.

Figure 333 shows a triangle which has been circumscribed with a circle. (The circle is drawn around it touching all three points.) The procedure to follow is similar to that used when drawing a circle to pass through three given points.

Figure 334 shows the methods used to draw a circle in isometric projection:

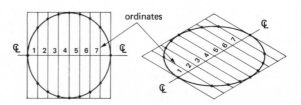

Figure 334   *Drawing a circle in isometric projection*

1   Construct a normal circle to the required radius.
2   Draw an isometric square, the lengths of the sides to be twice the radius.
3   Draw a centre line in both the circle and the square.
4   Divide both centre lines into a number of equal parts. Parallel lines are then drawn through these points and numbered. (These lines are called ordinates.)

5 The lengths of these lines should be measured from the centre line on the circle and transferred on to the square. This will give a series of points on the ordinates.

6 Draw a curved line to pass through all of the points.

Note: An isometric view of a circle will appear as an ellipse.

Figures 335 and 336 show the junction between two straight lines and an arc.

In Figure 335, the lines are at right angles. The method used to set out the arc is:

1 Draw lines AB and CD parallel to the straight lines, at a distance equal to the radius of the arc.

2 Draw the arc. The point where the parallel lines cross is the centre required.

Where the lines are not at right angles, as in Figure 336 a similar method is used to draw the arc. The difference is the addition of two extra lines to indicate the ends of the arc.

Note: The extra lines are in fact normals and must be at right angles to the parallel lines.

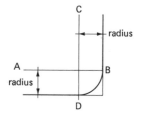

Figure 335 *Joining two lines at 90° with an arc*

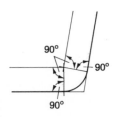

Figure 336 *Joining two lines at any angle with an arc*

Roofing geometry

Pitched roof geometry can be divided into three groups:

The development of roof surfaces.
Finding the true lengths of rafters, etc.
Finding the required angles for the cuts to the rafters and other components.

Figures 337, 338 and 339 show the plans, elevations and developments of three types of roof. Figure 337 is a lean-to roof. Figure 338 shows a gable-end roof which is rectangular in plan, and Figure 339 shows a gable-end roof which

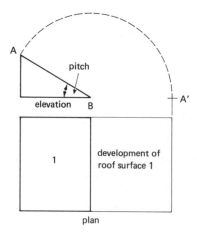

Figure 337 *Lean-to roof*

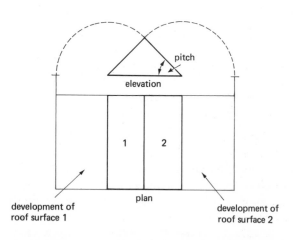

Figure 338 *Gable-end roof, rectangular in plan*

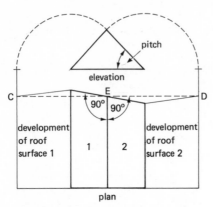

Figure 339   *Gable-end roof, splayed end in plan*

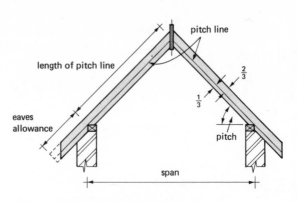

Figure 340   *Section through a simple roof*

has a splayed end in plan. The development of all three roofs is found in a similar way:

1 Swing the sloping surfaces of the roof AB down onto the horizontal plane with a compass.
2 Draw a vertical line down from A^1 to meet the two horizontal lines which have been extended from the plan. This gives the true shape or development of the roof surface.

   Note: When developing the surfaces of the splayed-end roof (Figure 339), the points C and D must be at right angles to point E, which is the end of the ridge.

Illustrated in Figure 340 is a section through a simple roof. It shows the following:

The *span*, which is from the outside of one wall-plate to the outside of the other wallplate.
The *pitch*, which can be in degrees or $\frac{\text{rise}}{\text{span}}$.
The *length of the pitch line*, which is measured between the corner of the wallplate and the centre line of the ridge board.
The *eaves allowance*, which is the length of rafter required to clear the brickwork and to provide the required eaves overhang.

In order to determine the true lengths and the angles for the cuts to the rafters, a scale drawing is required. Figure 341 is a scale drawing of the elevation of a roof. It shows the plumb and seat cuts, and also the true length of the pitch line of the rafter.

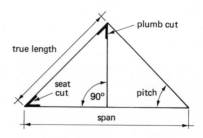

Figure 341   *Scale drawing of a roof elevation*

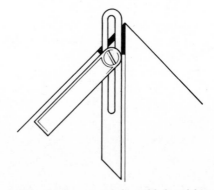

Figure 342   *Setting up an adjustable bevel from a scale drawing*

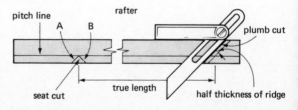

Figure 343   *Setting out a rafter*

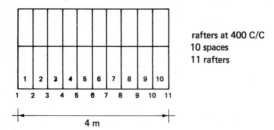

rafters at 400 C/C
10 spaces
11 rafters

Figure 344   *Finding the number of rafters in a roof*

In Figure 342 an adjustable bevel is being set up for a plumb cut from a scale drawing.

Shown in Figure 343 is a rafter being set out. The procedure for this should be as follows:

1   Mark pitch line on rafter.
2   Set adjustable bevel from drawing and mark plumb cut.
3   Determine the true length of pitch line from the drawing and mark on the rafter.
4   Mark seat cut. This consists of two lines, line (A) is a plumb cut and line (B) is a seat cut.
5   Re-mark plumb cut moving in half the thickness of the ridge board. (This is because the length of the pitch line extends to the centre line of the ridge.)

Note: The overhanging ends of the rafters are not normally marked out or cut until all of the rafters have been fixed in position. A string line is then run along the roof and the rafters are marked and cut to this line. This ensures that the ends of the rafters provide a straight line on which to fix the fascia board.

Shown in Figure 344 is a method used to find the number of rafters in a roof. The procedure is to divide the length of the roof by the centre to centre spacings of the rafters.

Example

Length of the roof   = 4 m
Spacing of the rafters = 0.4 m (centre to centre)
4 m ÷ 0.4 m   = 10
This means 10 spaces.

As there is always one more rafter than the number of spaces, there will be eleven rafters on each side of the roof, twenty-two rafters in all.

Self-assessment questions

1   The graphical symbol shown in Figure 345 represents
    (a) brickwork
    (b) prepared timber
    (c) sawn timber
    (d) hardcore

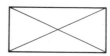

Figure 345   *Self-assessment question*

2   The abbreviation for softwood that complies with BS 1192 is
    (a) SW
    (b) swd
    (c) SFWD
    (d) sfwd

3   The drawing of a house, which is shown in Figure 346 has been produced in
    (a) third angle projection
    (b) isometric projection
    (c) first angle projection
    (d) oblique projection

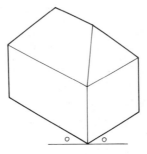

Figure 346   *Self-assessment question*

4   The angles marked O in Figure 346 should be drawn at
    (a) 30 degrees to the horizontal
    (b) 45 degrees to the horizontal
    (c) 30 degrees to the vertical
    (d) 45 degrees to the vertical

5 In order to determine the centre for the segmental arch shown in Figure 347 it is necessary to bisect
   (a) AD
   (b) AB
   (c) AC
   (d) DB

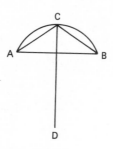

Figure 347   *Self-assessment question*

6 A quadrant of a circle has an area equal to
   (a) half of the circle
   (b) a quarter of the circle
   (c) three-quarters of the circle
   (d) one-third of the circle

7 A line which divides a quadrilateral into two triangles is called
   (a) a diagonal
   (b) a tangent
   (c) a bisection
   (d) an ordinate

8 A circle which is drawn in isometric projection will appear to be
   (a) trapezoidal
   (b) semicircular
   (c) parabolic
   (d) elliptical

9 When producing a drawing using first angle projection, the view from above is placed
   (a) above the front view
   (b) below the front view
   (c) to the left of the front view
   (d) to the right of the front view

10 The pitch line in a roof is measured from
    (a) the outside of one wallplate to the outside of the other wallplate
    (b) the outside of the wallplate to the outside of the ridge board
    (c) the outside of the wallplate to the centre line of the ridge board
    (d) the centre of the wallplate to the centre line of the ridge board

Answers to self-assessment questions

Chapter 1 Hand tools

1	(c)		6	(a)
2	(d)		7	(b)
3	(c)		8	(c)
4	(b)		9	(d)
5	(c)		10	(d)

Chapter 2 Woodworking machines and powered hand tools

1	(c)		6	(b)
2	(d)		7	(c)
3	(a)		8	(a)
4	(a)		9	(a)
5	(b)		10	(c)

Chapter 3 Materials

1	(c)		6	(b)
2	(b)		7	(a)
3	(a)		8	(d)
4	(a)		9	(c)
5	(d)		10	(a)

Chapter 4 Basic woodworking joints

1	(c)		6	(b)
2	(c)		7	(d)
3	(d)		8	(a)
4	(c)		9	(d)
5	(b)		10	(d)

Chapter 5 Joinery

1	(b)		6	(a)
2	(d)		7	(b)
3	(d)		8	(a)
4	(c)		9	(d)
5	(d)		10	(a)

Chapter 6 Construction work

1	(d)		6	(c)
2	(b)		7	(a)
3	(a)		8	(c)
4	(c)		9	(c)
5	(a)		10	(b)

Chapter 7 Basic drawing practice and geometry

1	(c)		6	(b)
2	(d)		7	(a)
3	(b)		8	(d)
4	(a)		9	(b)
5	(c)		10	(c)

Index